THE WIND CRACKED HIS WHIP,
THE STORM FLASHED A GUN,
AND THE ANIMAL-CLOUDS MARCHED ONE BY ONE
UNDER THE TENT OF THE SKY.

— Rowena Bastin Bennett.

UNDER THE TENT OF THE SKY

THE MACMILLAN COMPANY
NEW YORK · BOSTON · CHICAGO · DALLAS
ATLANTA · SAN FRANCISCO

MACMILLAN AND CO., Limited
LONDON · BOMBAY · CALCUTTA · MADRAS
MELBOURNE

THE MACMILLAN COMPANY
OF CANADA, Limited
TORONTO

UNDER THE TENT OF THE SKY

A COLLECTION of POEMS ABOUT ANIMALS LARGE AND SMALL

Selected by
JOHN E. BREWTON

· · · WITH DRAWINGS by

ROBERT LAWSON

THE MACMILLAN COMPANY

NEW YORK

MCMXL

TO

BETTY

ONCE FOUR, NOW ELEVEN

FOREWORD

This collection was begun when Betty was four and I was seven or so years younger than I am now. Now that Betty is eleven and I'm, oh, so much older, we are—for this is as much her book as mine—happy to give to you this collection of animal poems we have enjoyed together.

The subject—animals, all kinds, even some that never were—is so interesting and the poems so keenly delightful, we think, that we just had to share them with you.

We hope you like them.

March 1,
1937

JOHN EDMUND BREWTON
BETTY BREWTON

CONTENTS

[ix]

Animals Never Seen in Circus or Zoo

The Animal Store

Let's Pretend

In Fairyland

Beneath Man's Wings

Playmates

[xiii]

Animal Fancies

Animal Fun

[xv]

[xvi]

UNDER THE TENT OF THE SKY

CIRCUS CAVALCADE

Gaily plumed a horse and rider
Lead the circus cavalcade.

James S. Tippett.

CIRCUS PARADE

Here it comes! Here it comes!
I can hear the music playing;
I can hear the beating drums.

On parade! On parade!
Gaily plumed a horse and rider
Lead the circus cavalcade.

Knights in armor with their banners
Calmly riding by;
Horses hung with velvet trappings,
Stepping proudly high;
Circus wagons slowly clanking,
Drawn by six horse teams,
Red and gold and set with mirrors
Where the sunlight gleams;
Yawning lions in their cages;
Polar bear with swinging head;
Restless tiger pacing pacing
Back and forth with noiseless tread:
Horses snorting and cavorting
With wild yelling cowboy bands;
Dressed-up monkeys riding ponies,
Bowing as we clap our hands;
Herds of elephants and camels,
Marching one by one;
Troops of painted clowns advancing,
Playing tricks, and making fun.

At the end the steam calliope
Comes playing all too soon,
Saying the parade is over
As it pipes its wildest tune.

—*James S. Tippett*

[3]

A CIRCUS GARLAND

Parade

This is the day the circus comes
With blare of brass, with beating drums,
And clashing cymbals, and with roar
Of wild beasts never heard before
Within town limits. Spick and span
Will shine each gilded cage and van;
Cockades at every horse's head
Will nod, and riders dressed in red
Or blue trot by. There will be floats
In shapes like dragons, thrones and boats,
And clowns on stilts; freaks big and small,
Till leisurely and last of all
Camels and elephants will pass
Beneath our elms, along our grass.

The Performing Seal

Who is so proud
As not to feel
A secret awe
Before a seal
That keeps such sleek
And wet repose
While twirling candles
On his nose?

[4]

Gunga

With wrinkled hide and great frayed ears,
Gunga, the elephant, appears.
Colored like city smoke he goes
As gingerly on blunted toes
As if he held the earth in trust
And feared to hurt the very dust.

Equestrienne

See, they are clearing the sawdust course
For the girl in pink on the milk-white horse.
Her spangles twinkle; his pale flanks shine,
Every hair of his tail is fine
And bright as a comet's; his mane blows free,
And she points a toe and bends a knee,
And while his hoofbeats fall like rain
Over and over and over again.
And nothing that moves on land or sea
Will seem so beautiful to me
As the girl in pink on the milk-white horse
Cantering over the sawdust course.

Epilogue

Nothing now to mark the spot
But a littered vacant lot;
Sawdust in a heap, and there
Where the ring was, grass worn bare
In a circle, scuffed and brown,
And a paper hoop the clown
Made his little dog jump through,
And a pygmy pony-shoe.

—Rachel Field

[5]

THE CIRCUS

Friday came and the circus was there,
And Mother said that the twins and I
And Charles and Clarence and all of us
Could go out and see the parade go by.

And there were wagons with pictures on,
And you never could guess what they had inside,
Nobody could guess, for the doors were shut,
And there was a dog that a monkey could ride.

A man on the top of a sort of cart
Was clapping his hands and making a talk.
And the elephant came—he can step pretty far—
It made us laugh to see him walk.

Three beautiful ladies came riding by,
And each one had on a golden dress,
And each one had a golden whip.
They were queens of Sheba, I guess.

A big wild man was in a cage,
And he had some snakes going over his feet
And somebody said "He eats them alive!"
But I didn't see him eat.

—Elizabeth Madox Roberts

AT THE CIRCUS

The Elephants

With their trunks the elephants
Hold hands in a long row—
Their little eyes so quick and wise,
Their feet so big and slow.
They climb on top of things and then,
When they are told, climb down again.

Bare-back Rider

There isn't a prettier sight, I think,
Than a pony that's white and a lady that's pink:
The pony so frisky and stepping so high,
The lady so smiling as they go by,
The lady so tip-toe on her toes,
The pony, his bridle dressed up with a rose,
The lady and pony both liking to be
Riding around for the world to see.

The Seals

The seals all flap
Their shining flips
And bounce balls on
Their nosey tips,
And beat a drum,
And catch a bar,
And wriggle with
How pleased they are.
                    —*Dorothy Aldis*

[7]

HOLDING HANDS

Elephants walking
Along the trails

Are holding hands
By holding tails.

Trunks and tails
Are handy things

When elephants walk
In Circus rings.

Elephants work
And elephants play

And elephants walk
And feel so gay.

And when they walk—
It never fails

They're holding hands
By holding tails.
                    —*Lenore M. Link*

CIRCUS

The brass band blares,
The naphtha flares,
The sawdust smells,
Showmen ring bells,
And oh! right into the circus-ring
Comes such a lovely, lovely thing,
A milk-white pony with flying tress,
And a beautiful lady,
A beautiful lady,
A *beautiful* lady in a pink dress!
The red-and-white clown
For joy tumbles down,
Like a pink rose
Round she goes
On her tip-toes
With the pony under—
And then, oh, wonder!
The pony his milk-white tresses droops,
And the beautiful lady,
The *beautiful* lady,
Flies like a bird through the paper hoops!
The red-and-white clown for joy falls dead.
Then he waggles his feet and stands on his head,
And the little boys on the twopenny seats
Scream with laughter and suck their sweets.

—Eleanor Farjeon

THE DAY OF THE CIRCUS HORSE

It was a fiery circus horse
    That ramped and stamped and neighed,
Till every creature in its course
    Fled, frightened and dismayed.
The chickens on the roadway's edge
    Arose and flapped their wings,
And making for the sheltering hedge
    Flew off like crazy things.

Nor iron gates nor fences barred
    That mettled steed's career.
It galloped right across our yard
    And filled us all with fear;
And when it tossed its head and ran
    Straight through the pantry door,
Cook almost dropped her frying-pan
    Upon the kitchen floor!

It neighed and pranced and wheeled about
    And scampered off, but then
We scarcely saw the creature out
    When it was in again.
And so throughout the livelong day
    Through house and yard and street,
That charger held its fearsome way
    And only stopped to eat.

But when, at dusk, a little lame,
   It slowly climbed the stairs,
Behold! a gentle lady came
   And made it say its prayers.
Now, what a wondrous change you see!
   'Sh! Come and take a peep—
Here lies, as tame as tame can be,
   A little boy, asleep!
              —*Thomas Augustine Daly*

OUR CIRCUS

We had a circus in our shed
(Admission, three new pins a head)
And every girl and boy I know
Is talking yet about our show.

They laughed so hard at Fatty Brown
When he came out to be the clown,
That all the neighbors ran to see
Whatever such a noise could be.

Our tin-pan and mouth-organ band
Played tunes that sounded simply grand;
We had a truly sawdust ring,
Pink lemonade, 'n everything.

The big menagerie was nice:
Three cats, one dog, and five white mice,
A parrot that Bill's uncle lent;
All underneath a bedspread tent.

Then Ned and Buster took a sheet
That covered them from head to feet
And made a horse that kicked and pranced
And when it heard the band, it danced.

And Sally Ann was "Bareback Queen"!
No finer rider could be seen;
She stood right up, and looked so proud,
But kissed her hand to all the crowd.

We took some chalk—blue, green, and red—
And made a "Tattooed Man" of Fred;
Jim juggled lighted cigarettes,
And Tom turned double somersets.

We had tall stilts—and flying rings—
And lots and lots of other things—
And every boy and girl I know
Said yes, it was a *dandy* show!
                              —*Laura Lee Randall*

I WENT DOWN TO THE ZOO

But I gave buns to the elephant when I went down to the Zoo.

A A Milne

SERIOUS OMISSION

I know that there are dragons,
St. George's, Jason's, too,
And many modern dragons
With scales of green and blue;

But though I've been there many times
And carefully looked through,
I can't find a dragon
In the cages at the zoo!

—*John Farrar*

LION

Lion, you were once the King
Of every single living thing,
In forests where the wild beasts prey
Upon each other night and day,
Your fearful roaring used to make
All God's other creatures quake,
When in the jungle with a rush
You crashed through trees and underbrush:
But now you're prisoned in the Zoo,
And nobody's afraid of you.
You've thrown yourself upon the floor
Too sorrowful to even roar,
Lying in the dust, instead
Of holding high your kingly head.
O lion, you were made to be
Proud, majestic, wild and free;
Jungle, forest, glade and fen
You will never see again.
Rest your poor head upon the floor—
Try to sleep a little more.

—*Mary Britton Miller*

THE ELEPHANT

Here comes the elephant
Swaying along
With his cargo of children
All singing a song:
To the tinkle of laughter
He goes on his way,
And his cargo of children
Have crowned him with may.
His legs are in leather
And padded his toes:
He can root up an oak
With a whisk of his nose:
With a wave of his trunk
And a turn of his chin
He can pull down a house,
Or pick up a pin.
Beneath his gray forehead
A little eye peers;
Of what is he thinking
Between those wide ears?
Of what does he think?
If he wishes to tease,
He could twirl his keeper
Over the trees:
If he were not kind,
He could play cup and ball
With Robert and Helen,
And Uncle Paul:
But that gray forehead,
Those crinkled ears,
Have learned to be kind
In a hundred years:

And so with the children
He goes on his way
To the tinkle of laughter
And crowned with the may.
                    —*Herbert Asquith*

THE ELEPHANT

When people call this beast to mind,
    They marvel more and more
At such a *little* tail behind,
    So LARGE a trunk before.
                    —*Hilaire Belloc*

CAMEL

O camel in the zoo,
You don't do any of the things
They tell me that you used to do
In Egypt, and in other lands,
Carrying potentates and kings
Across the burning desert sands
With gorgeous trappings made of blue
And scarlet silks to cover you.

Your humps are carried on your back
Just the way they always were,
You thrust your old head up and back,
And make your neck go in and out,
And spill the foam upon your fur,
And writhe and jerk and rear about,
But kneel no more upon the sands
To mount the kings of eastern lands.
                    —*Mary Britton Miller*

THE PLAINT OF THE CAMEL

Canary-birds feed on sugar and seed,
    Parrots have crackers to crunch;
And as for the poodles, they tell me the noodles
    Have chickens and cream for their lunch.
        But there's never a question
        About MY digestion—
    ANYTHING does for me!

Cats, you're aware, can repose in a chair,
    Chickens can roost upon rails;
Puppies are able to sleep in a stable,
    And oysters can slumber in pails.
        And no one supposes
        A poor Camel dozes—
    ANY PLACE does for me!

Lambs are enclosed where it's never exposed,
    Coops are constructed for hens;
Kittens are treated to houses well heated,
    And pigs are protected by pens.
        But a Camel comes handy
        Wherever it's sandy—
    ANYWHERE does for me!

People would laugh if you rode a giraffe,
    Or mounted the back of an ox;
It's nobody's habit to ride on a rabbit,
    Or try to bestraddle a fox.
        But as for a Camel, he's
        Ridden by families—
    ANY LOAD does for me!

A snake is as round as a hole in the ground,
  And weasels are wavy and sleek;
And no alligator could ever be straighter
  Than lizards that live in a creek,
    But a Camel's all lumpy
    And bumpy and humpy—
  ANY SHAPE does for me!
                    —*Charles Edward Carryl*

THE MONKEYS

Sing a song of monkeys
A jolly bunch of monkeys!
Leaping, swinging in their cages
Looking wise as ancient sages,
Nonchalant and care free manner
Nibbling peanut or banana,
Every day is just another
To a monkey or his brother.

Sing a song of monkeys,
Happy, merry monkeys,
If you're ever tired or blue
I can tell you what to do!
Let the monkeys at the Zoo
Make a monkey out of you!
                    —*Edith Osborne Thompson*

EXCUSE US, ANIMALS IN THE ZOO

Excuse us, Animals in the Zoo,
I'm sure we're very rude to you;
Into your private house we stare
And never ask you if you care;
And never ask you if you mind.
Perhaps we really are not kind;
I think it must be hard to stay
And have folks looking in all day,
I wouldn't like my house that way.

Excuse us, Animals in the Zoo,
I'm sure we're very rude to you;
Suppose you all to our house came
And stared at us and called our name.
I hardly think we'd like it at all
In a house that didn't have a wall.
No wonder you pace up and down the floor
And growl a little or even roar—
I'm sure if 'twere we, we'd growl much more.

Excuse us, Animals in the Zoo,
I'm sure we're very rude to you.
                              —*Annette Wynne*

ANIMALS NEVER SEEN IN CIRCUS OR ZOO

Purple horses with orange manes,
Elephants pink and blue,
Tigers and lions that never were seen,
In circus parade or zoo!

Rachel Field.

MERRY-GO-ROUND

Purple horses with orange manes,
    Elephants pink and blue,
Tigers and lions that never were seen
    In circus parade or zoo!
Bring out your money and choose your steed,
    And prance to delightsome sound.
What fun if the world would turn some day
    Into a Merry-Go-Round!
                —*Rachel Field*

ANIMAL CRACKERS

Animal crackers, and cocoa to drink,
That is the finest of suppers, I think;
When I'm grown up and can have what I please
I think I shall always insist upon these.

What do *you* choose when you're offered a treat?
When Mother says, "What would you like best to eat?"
Is it waffles and syrup, or cinnamon toast?
It's cocoa and animals that *I* love the most!

The kitchen's the cosiest place that I know:
The kettle is singing, the stove is aglow,
And there in the twilight, how jolly to see
The cocoa and animals waiting for me.

Daddy and Mother dine later in state,
With Mary to cook for them, Susan to wait;
But they don't have nearly as much fun as I
Who eat in the kitchen with Nurse standing by;
And Daddy once said, he would like to be me
Having cocoa and animals once more for tea!
                                    —*Christopher Morley*

THE TEAPOT DRAGON

There's a dragon on our teapot,
    With a long and crinkly tail,
His claws are like a pincer-bug,
    His wings are like a sail;

His tongue is always sticking out,
    And so I used to think
He must be very hungry, or
    He wanted tea to drink.

But once when Mother wasn't round
    I dipped my fingers in,
And when I pulled them out I found
    I'd blistered all the skin.

Now when I see the dragon crawl
    Around our china pot,
I know he's burned his tongue because
    The water is so hot.
                                    —*Rupert Sargent Holland*

TEMPLE BAR

London's full of statues—
    Some of them are kings,
And some of them are gentlemen
    Who just did clever things;
And some of them have horses,
    Some only sit or stand,
And some are rather queerly dressed,
    And some are very grand.

But what, oh, what did the dragon do
That he was given a statue too?

His wings are long and pointed,
    He's got a lot of scales,
He's very like St. George's
    And those in fairy tales;
He looks a little haughty,
    His tail is in the air;
But nobody can tell me
    The reason he is there.

Though dragons in the stories
    Were as bad as they could be
And people had to kill them
    To set Princesses free,
I'm sure he was a good one,
    But they haven't put his name,
And not a word about him,
    And I think it is a shame.

And I wish so much, so much that I knew
What the dragon did really do.
               —*Rose Fyleman*

TRAFALGAR SQUARE

Nelson's on a column—
  Such a high, high place
That only birds that fly there
Or airmen who go by there
  Could ever see his face.

The lions at the bottom,
  They guard him night and day;
Their manes are fine and frilly,
But it does seem rather silly
  That they're so far away.

If ever he should need them
  They wouldn't be much good;
They're kind and wise and solemn,
But they'd never climb that column—
  I don't see how they *could*.

              —*Rose Fyleman*

THE DUEL

The gingham dog and the calico cat
Side by side on the table sat;
'T was half-past twelve, and (what do you think!)
Nor one nor t' other had slept a wink!
    The old Dutch clock and the Chinese plate
    Appeared to know as sure as fate
There was going to be a terrible spat.
        (*I wasn't there; I simply state
        What was told to me by the Chinese plate!*)

The gingham dog went "bow-wow-wow!"
And the calico cat replied "mee-ow!"
The air was littered, an hour or so,
With bits of gingham and calico,
    While the old Dutch clock in the chimney-place
    Up with its hands before its face,
For it always dreaded a family row!
        (*Now mind: I'm only telling you
        What the old Dutch clock declares is true!*)

The Chinese plate looked very blue,
And wailed, "Oh, dear! what shall we do!"
But the gingham dog and the calico cat
Wallowed this way and tumbled that,
    Employing every tooth and claw
    In the awfullest way you ever saw—
And, oh! how the gingham and calico flew!
        (*Don't fancy I exaggerate—
        I got my news from the Chinese plate!*)

Next morning, where the two had sat
They found no trace of dog or cat;
And some folks think unto this day
That burglars stole that pair away!
  But the truth about the cat and pup
  Is this: they ate each other up!
Now what do you really think of that!
    (*The old Dutch clock it told me so,
    And that is how I came to know.*)
                        —*Eugene Field*

THE
ANIMAL STORE

If I had a hundred dollars to spend,
Or maybe a little more,
I'd hurry as fast as my legs would go
Straight to the animal store.

Rachel Field.

THE ANIMAL STORE

If I had a hundred dollars to spend,
  Or maybe a little more,
I'd hurry as fast as my legs would go
  Straight to the animal store.

I wouldn't say, "How much for this or that?"—
  "What kind of a dog is he?"
I'd buy as many as rolled an eye,
  Or wagged a tail at me!

I'd take the hound with the drooping ears
  That sits by himself alone;
Cockers and Cairns and wobbly pups
  For to be my very own.

I might buy a parrot all red and green,
  And the monkey I saw before,
If I had a hundred dollars to spend,
  Or maybe a little more.
                              —*Rachel Field*

PEOPLE BUY A LOT OF THINGS

People buy a lot of things—
Carts and balls and nails and rings,
But I would buy a bird that sings.

I would buy a bird that sings and let it sing for me,
And let it sing of flying things and mating in a tree,
And then I'd open wide the cage, and set the singer free.
                              —*Annette Wynne*

SHOP WINDOWS

Mother likes the frocks and hats
And pretty stuffs and coloured mats.

Daddy never, never looks
At anything but pipes and books.

Auntie's fond of chains and rings
And all the sparkly diamond things.

Richard likes machines the best;
He doesn't care about the rest.

Nannie always loves to stop
In front of every single shop.

But I don't want to wait for a minute
Till we get to the one with the puppy dogs in it.

—*Rose Fyleman*

LET'S PRETEND

Let's pretend we're elephants
Who trample down tall grass
Who force their way through jungles
And trumpet as they pass.

James S. Tippett.

WILD BEASTS

I will be a lion
  And you shall be a bear,
And each of us will have a den
  Beneath a nursery chair;
And you must growl and growl and growl,
  And I will roar and roar,
And then—why, then—you'll growl again,
  And I will roar some more!
                              —*Evaleen Stein*

LIONS RUNNING OVER THE GREEN

  Lions running over the green,
  Fiercest of creatures that ever were seen,
  Chasing Tom and Dick and Sue—
  I hope they won't be caught, don't you?

  The lions chase them through the gate,
  But Sue cries out: "O lions, wait,
  My shoe's untied!" One lion then
  Ties the lacing up again.

  And after that the chase goes on
  Until the afternoon is gone—
  The fiercest creatures ever seen,
  Lions running over the green!
                              —*Annette Wynne*

RADIATOR LIONS

George lives in an apartment and
His mother will not let
Him keep a dog or polliwog
Or rabbit for a pet.

So he has Radiator Lions.
(The parlor is the zoo.)
They love to fight but will not bite
Unless he tells them to.

And days when it is very cold
And he can't go outdoors
They glower and they lower and they
Crouch upon all fours.

And roar most awful roarings and
Gurgle loud and mad.
Up their noses water goeses—
That's what makes them bad.

But he loves Radiator Lions!
He's glad, although they're wild,
He hasn't dogs and polliwogs
Like any other child!

—*Dorothy Aldis*

SATURDAY TOWELS

Under the bed
Away upstairs,
I like to pretend
Is a den for bears.

It's cool up there
When the yard is hot,
Sometimes it's dusty
And sometimes it's not.

So I lie very still
Hardly breathing at all
Till I hear black shoes
Coming down the hall,

Till Mary brings in
The Saturday towels.
Then I scramble out
With the awfullest yowls,

With the awfullest, awfullest
Sort of a roar,
And she drops the towels
And runs for the door.

Then I laugh and I laugh,
For, don't you see,
She thinks it's a bear,
But it's only Me!
            —*Lysbeth Boyd Borie*

THE RACE

My tricycle's a camel
With thickly padded feet.

My wagon is a charger
That clatters down the street.

I'd like to ride them both at once
To see which one would beat!
                              —*Aileen Fisher*

THE BEAR HUNT

I played I was two polar bears
Who lived inside a cave of chairs,

And Brother was the hunter-man
Who tried to shoot us when we ran.

The ten-pins made good bones to gnaw,
I held them down beneath my paw.

Of course, I had to kill him quick
Before he shot me with his stick.

So all the cave fell down, you see,
On Brother and the bones and me—

So then he said he wouldn't play—
But it was tea-time, anyway!
                              —*Margaret Widdemer*

SITTING HERE

Sitting here
In our usual chairs
It's pleasant to think
Of polar bears,

Of polar bears
Amid ice-floes,
Dog sleds, and flat-faced
Eskimos.

It's pleasant to think,
On the other hand,
Of monkeys who live
In a tropical land,

And chatter and peer
At the forest floor
Where elephants stamp
And lions roar.

As high as the strong-winged
Eagles fly
Our little thoughts climb
To pierce the sky.

And deep in the sea
As fishes sink
A child may go
If a child will think.

High and low
And far and wide
Swift and nimble
A thought will ride,

But what it brings back
At the saddle bow,
Only the mind that sent it
Will know.
—Elizabeth Coatsworth

AT NIGHT

When I go to bed at night
The darkness is a bear.
He crouches in the corner,
Or hides behind a chair;
The one who tells me stories—
She does not know he's there.

But when she kisses me good-night,
And darkness starts to creep
Across the floor, why, then I see
It's just a woolly sheep,
That nibbles at my rugs awhile
Before we go to sleep.
—Anne Blackwell Payne

IN
FAIRYLAND

When I went to Fairyland, visiting the Queen,
I rode upon a peacock, blue and gold and green.

Rose Fyleman.

TIMOTHY

My cat Timothy who has such lovely eyes
Is really not a cat at all; it's only a disguise.
A witch cast a spell on him a long time since
And changed him to a pussy-cat; but once he was a Prince.

On warm clear nights when a big moon is out
He steps into the garden and never turns about,
But walks down the path with his quiet proud air—
He knows that the fairies are waiting out there.

The fairies go a-dancing, a-dancing in a ring,
He sits in the middle with a crown like a king,
High on a throne in the middle of the grass,
And the fairies stop capering to curtsey as they pass.

Some day, some day when the spell is done
He will be a Prince again. *Won't* that be fun?
He will come to seek me and kiss my lily hand
And take me on his foaming steed to reign in fairyland.

—Rose Fyleman

THE COCK

The kindly cock is the fairies' friend,
He warns them when their revels must end;
He never forgets to give the word,
For the cock is a thoroughly punctual bird.

And since he grieves that he never can fly,
Like all the other birds, up in the sky,
The fairies put him now and again
High on a church for a weather-vane.

Little for sun or for rain he cares;
He turns about with the proudest airs
And chuckles with joy as the clouds go past
To think he is up in the sky at last.

—Rose Fyleman

THE CUCKOO

The cuckoo is a tell-tale,
  A mischief-making bird;
He flies to East, he flies to West
And whispers into every nest
  The wicked things he's heard;
He loves to spread his naughty lies,
He laughs about it as he flies;
"Cuckoo," he cries, "cuckoo, cuckoo,
  It's true, it's true."

And when the fairies catch him
  His busy wings they dock,
They shut him up for evermore
(He may not go beyond the door)
  Inside a wooden clock;
Inside a wooden clock he cowers
And has to tell the proper hours—
"Cuckoo," he cries, "cuckoo, cuckoo,
  It's true, it's true."

—Rose Fyleman

THE CANARY

He used to be a fairy once,
  A little singing fairy;
He would not work, he would not play,
He only sat and sang all day—
  So now he's a canary.

They sent him out of fairyland,
  They sent him here to me
The day that I was six years old;
His little house of shining gold
  Hangs in the nursery.

He's taught me lots of lovely things
  I never should have guessed;
He's told me what they say and do
(They all have wings—it's really true)
  And how the Queen is dressed.

He flits about the house at night
  A little lonely fairy;
But nobody is there to see,
And no one knows—excepting me—
  He's not a real canary.   —*Rose Fyleman*

AN EXPLANATION OF THE GRASSHOPPER

The Grasshopper, the Grasshopper,
  I will explain to you:—
He is the Brownies' racehorse,
  The fairies' Kangaroo.   —*Vachel Lindsay*

THE ELF AND THE DORMOUSE

Under a toadstool crept a wee Elf,
Out of the rain to shelter himself.

Under the toadstool, sound asleep,
Sat a big Dormouse all in a heap.

Trembled the wee Elf, frightened, and yet
Fearing to fly away lest he get wet.

To the next shelter—maybe a mile!
Sudden the wee Elf smiled a wee smile,

Tugged till the toadstool toppled in two.
Holding it over him, gaily he flew.

Soon he was safe home, dry as could be.
Soon woke the Dormouse—"Good gracious me!

"Where is my toadstool?" loud he lamented.
—And that's how umbrellas first were invented.
                                        —*Oliver Herford*

WHERE THE BEE SUCKS

Where the bee sucks, there suck I:
  In a cowslip's bell I lie;
There I couch when owls do cry.
  On the bat's back I do fly
  After summer merrily;
    Merrily, merrily shall I live now,
    Under the blossom that hangs on the bough.
                                  —*William Shakespeare*

FAIRY AEROPLANES

The fairies, too, have aeroplanes,
To carry them about,
That swoop, and soar, and dart, and dip,
And circle in and out.

So when their little wings are tired,
They summon one of these,
And sail above the garden beds
Or anywhere they please.

The fairies' aeroplanes are safe
And never do capsize,
They're very beautiful and gay,
Because they're butterflies.

—Anne Blackwell Payne

THE FAIRY FROCK

It's primrose petals for a gown,
For sempstress spiders three,
It's gossamer and thistledown
To make my frock for me.
Then hie thee straight to cobbler toad
Beneath the hornbeam tree
Beyond the turning of the road
To shape my shoes for me.
Then put a dewdrop in my hair,
Fetch me my cobweb shawl,
And call my cricket coach and pair
To drive me to the ball!

—Katharine Morse

SPIDER WEBS

The spiders were busy last night;
From every fence and tree
They hung their lacy webs
For all the world to see.

The mist was busy too;
In the stillness of the night
It strung the spider webs with pearls
To catch the morning light.

One spider wove a web
Like frost on a window pane;
Another one spun a single thread
That looks like a jeweled chain.

Motionless hang the webs,
By the quiet sunbeams kissed;
A fairy world was made last night
By the spiders and the mist.

—James S. Tippett

BENEATH
MAN'S WINGS

Go out to feed the living things
Man has taken beneath his wings.
Robert P. Tristram Coffin.

IN THE BARNYARD

In the barnyard chickens walk,—
They jerk their heads and peck and talk,
While yellow ducklings run around
Like butter balls upon the ground,
And some geese, tremendous proud,
Point their noses at a cloud.

—Dorothy Aldis

FAMILIAR FRIENDS

The horses, the pigs,
And the chickens,
The turkeys, the ducks,
And the sheep!
I can see all my friends
From my window
As soon as I waken
From sleep.

The cat on the fence
Is out walking.
The geese have gone down
For a swim.
The pony comes trotting
Right up to the gate;
He knows I have candy
For him.

The cows in the pasture
Are switching
Their tails to keep off
The flies.
And the old mother dog
Has come out in the yard
With five pups to give me
A surprise.

—*James S. Tippett*

THE MILK-CART PONY

The milk-cart pony in the street
    Is spotted white and brown,
He frisks his mane, he kicks his feet,
    And rattles through the town.

His milk-cans glitter in the sun,
    His harness clinks and rings,
The milk-cart pony on the run
    Must think of lively things.

Perhaps he thinks of circus-tents
    And ladies in top hats,
And orange-peel and sawdust scents,
    And clowns and acrobats.

Perhaps he thinks of Derby Day
    With crowds upon the course
All shouting loud *Hip hip hooray!*
    Here comes the winning horse!

Perhaps he thinks of Dartymoor
  Where he was once a child.
And on the purple-heather floor
  The ponies still run wild.

Well, nobody knows *what* he thinks,
  This little skewbald clown,
Who bears our night and morning drinks
  So noisily through town!
                              —*Eleanor Farjeon*

HORSE

His bridle hung around the post;
The sun and the leaves made spots come down;
I looked close at him through the fence;
The post was drab and he was brown.

His nose was long and hard and still,
And on his lip were specks like chalk.
But once he opened up his eyes,
And he began to talk.

He didn't talk out with his mouth;
He didn't talk with words or noise.
The talk was there along his nose;
It seemed and then it was.

He said the day was hot and slow,
And he said he didn't like the flies;
They made him have to shake his skin,
And they got drowned in his eyes.

[53]

He said that drab was just about
The same as brown, but he was not
A post, he said, to hold a fence.
"I'm horse," he said, "that's what!"

And then he shut his eyes again.
As still as they had been before.
He said for me to run along
And not to bother him any more.

—Elizabeth Madox Roberts

NICHOLAS NYE

Thistle and darnel and dock grew there,
　　And a bush, in the corner, of may,
On the orchard wall I used to sprawl,
　　In the blazing heat of the day;
Half asleep and half awake,
　　While the birds went twittering by,
And nobody there my lone to share
　　But Nicholas Nye.

Nicholas Nye was lean and grey,
　　Lame of a leg and old,
More than a score of donkey's years
　　He had seen since he was foaled;
He munched the thistles, purple and spiked,
　　Would sometimes stoop and sigh,
And turn to his head, as if he said,
　　"Poor Nicholas Nye!"

Alone with his shadows he'd drowse in the meadow,
  Lazily swinging his tail,
At break of day he used to bray,—
  Not much too hearty and hale;
But a wonderful gumption was under his skin,
  And a clear calm light in his eye,
And once in a while: he'd smile:—
  Would Nicholas Nye.

Seem to be smiling at me, he would,
  From his bush, in the corner, of may,—
Bony and ownerless, widowed and worn,
  Knobble-kneed, lonely and grey;
And over the grass would seem to pass
  'Neath the deep dark blue of the sky,
Something much better than words between me
  And Nicholas Nye.

But dusk would come in the apple boughs,
  The green of the glow-worm shine,
The birds in nest would crouch to rest,
  And home I'd trudge to mine;
And there, in the moonlight, dark with dew,
  Asking not wherefore nor why,
Would brood like a ghost, and as still as a post,
  Old Nicholas Nye.
                              —*Walter de la Mare*

STOPPING BY WOODS ON A SNOWY EVENING

  Whose woods these are I think I know.
  His house is in the village though;
  He will not see me stopping here
  To watch his woods fill up with snow.

The little horse must think it queer
To stop without a farmhouse near
Between the woods and frozen lake
The darkest evening of the year.

He gives his harness bells a shake
To ask if there is some mistake.
The only other sound's the sweep
Of easy wind and downy flake.

The woods are lovely, dark and deep.
But I have promises to keep,
And miles to go before I sleep,
And miles to go before I sleep.

—*Robert Frost*

THE COW

Thank you, pretty cow, that made
Pleasant milk to soak my bread,
Every day and every night,
Warm, and fresh, and sweet, and white.

Do not chew the hemlock rank,
Growing on the weedy bank;
But the yellow cowslips eat,
They will make it very sweet.

Where the purple violet grows,
Where the bubbling water flows,
Where the grass is fresh and fine,
Pretty cow, go there and dine.

—*Ann Taylor*

THE COW

The friendly cow all red and white,
    I love with all my heart:
She gives me cream with all her might,
    To eat with apple-tart.

She wanders lowing here and there,
    And yet she cannot stray,
All in the pleasant open air,
    The pleasant light of day;

And blown by all the winds that pass
    And wet with all the showers,
She walks among the meadow grass
    And eats the meadow flowers.
                    —*Robert Louis Stevenson*

THE MILK JUG

(The Kitten Speaks)

The Gentle Milk Jug blue and white
    I love with all my soul,
She pours herself with all her might
    To fill my breakfast bowl.

All day she sits upon the shelf,
    She does not jump or climb—
She only waits to pour herself
    When 'tis my supper-time.

And when the Jug is empty quite,
    I shall not mew in vain,
The Friendly Cow, all red and white,
    Will fill her up again.

                        —*Oliver Herford*

THE PASTURE

I'm going out to clean the pasture spring;
I'll only stop to rake the leaves away
(And wait to watch the water clear, I may):
I sha'n't be gone long.—You come too.

I'm going out to fetch the little calf
That's standing by the mother. It's so young
It totters when she licks it with her tongue.
I sha'n't be gone long.—You come too.

                        —*Robert Frost*

WHEN THE COWS COME HOME

When the cows come home the milk is coming,
Honey's made while the bees are humming;
Duck and drake on the rushy lake,
And the deer live safe in the breezy brake;
And timid, funny, brisk little bunny
Winks his nose and sits all sunny.

                        —*Christina G. Rossetti*

MILKING TIME

When supper time is almost come,
But not quite here, I cannot wait,
And so I take my china mug
And go down by the milking gate.

The cow is always eating shucks
And spilling off the little silk.
Her purple eyes are big and soft—
She always smells like milk.

And Father takes my mug from me,
And then he makes the stream come out.
I see it going in my mug
And foaming all about.

And when it's piling very high,
And when some little streams commence
To run and drip along the sides,
He hands it to me through the fence.
            —*Elizabeth Madox Roberts*

ON THE GRASSY BANKS

On the grassy banks
Lambkins at their pranks;
Woolly sisters, woolly brothers,
    Jumping off their feet,
While their woolly mothers
    Watch by them and bleat.
            —*Christina G. Rossetti*

THE SHEEP

Lazy sheep, pray tell me why
In the pleasant field you lie,
Eating grass and daisies white
From the morning till the night?
Everything can something do;
But what kind of use are you?

Nay, my little master, nay,
Do not serve me so, I pray.
Don't you see the wool that grows
On my back to make you clothes?
Cold, and very cold, you'd get,
If I did not give you it.

True, it seems a pleasant thing
To nip the daisies in the spring;
But many chilly nights I pass
On the cold and dewy grass,
Or pick a scanty dinner, where
All the common's brown and bare.

Then the farmer comes at last,
When the merry spring is past,
Cuts my woolly coat away,
To warm you in the winter's day:
Little master, this is why
In the pleasant fields I lie.

—*Ann Taylor*

THE LAMB

Little Lamb, who made thee?
Dost thou know who made thee?
Gave thee life, and bid thee feed,
By the stream and o'er the mead;
Gave thee clothing of delight,
Softest clothing, woolly, bright;
Gave thee such a tender voice,
Making all the vales rejoice?
Little Lamb, who made thee?
Dost thou know who made thee?

Little Lamb, I'll tell thee,
Little Lamb, I'll tell thee:
He is callèd by thy name,
For He calls Himself a Lamb.
He is meek, and He is mild;
He became a little child.
I a child, and thou a lamb,
We are callèd by His name.
Little Lamb, God bless thee!
Little Lamb, God bless thee!
—*William Blake*

CHANTICLEER

High and proud on the barnyard fence
Walks rooster in the morning.
He shakes his comb, he shakes his tail
And gives his daily warning.

"Get up, you lazy boys and girls,
It's time you should be dressing!"
I wonder if he keeps a clock,
Or if he's only guessing.

—John Farrar

THE CHICKENS

Said the first little chicken,
    With a queer little squirm,
"I wish I could find
    A fat little worm."

Said the next little chicken,
    With an odd little shrug,
"I wish I could find
    A fat little slug."

Said the third little chicken,
    With a sharp little squeal,
"I wish I could find
    Some nice yellow meal."

Said the fourth little chicken,
    With a small sigh of grief,
"I wish I could find
    A little green leaf."

Said the fifth little chicken,
    With a faint little moan,
"I wish I could find
    A wee gravel stone."

"Now, see here," said the mother,
    From the green garden patch,
"If you want any breakfast,
    Just come here and scratch."
            —Author Unknown

THE HENS

The night was coming very fast;
It reached the gate as I ran past.

The pigeons had gone to the tower of the church
And all the hens were on their perch,

Up in the barn, and I thought I heard
A piece of a little purring word.

I stopped inside, waiting and staying,
To try to hear what the hens were saying.

They were asking something, that was plain,
Asking it over and over again.

One of them moved and turned around,
Her feathers made a ruffled sound,

A ruffled sound, like a bushful of birds,
And she said her little asking words.

She pushed her head close into her wing,
But nothing answered anything.
            —Elizabeth Madox Roberts

[63]

MRS. PECK-PIGEON

Mrs. Peck-Pigeon
Is picking for bread,
Bob-bob-bob
Goes her little round head.
Tame as a pussy-cat
In the street,
Step-step-step
Go her little red feet.
With her little red feet
And her little round head,
Mrs. Peck-Pigeon
Goes picking for bread.
                    —*Eleanor Farjeon*

SWIMMING

When all the days are hot and long
And robin bird has ceased his song,
I go swimming every day
And have the finest kind of play.

I've learned to dive and I can float
As easily as does a boat;
I splash and plunge and laugh and shout
Till Daddy tells me to come out.

It's much too soon; I'd like to cry
For I can see the ducks go by,
And Daddy Duck—how I love him—
He lets his children swim and swim!

I feel that I would be in luck
If I could only be a duck!
                    —*Clinton Scollard*

DUCKS' DITTY

All along the backwater,
Through the rushes tall,
Ducks are a-dabbling,
Up tails all!

Ducks' tails, drakes' tails,
Yellow feet a-quiver,
Yellow bills all out of sight
Busy in the river!

Slushy green undergrowth
Where the roach swim—
Here we keep our larder,
Cool and full and dim.

Everyone for what he likes!
We like to be
Heads down, tails up,
Dabbling free!

High in the blue above
Swifts whirl and call—
We are down a-dabbling,
Up tails all!
                    —*Kenneth Grahame*

DUCKS AT DAWN

"Quack! Quack!"
Said seven ducks at dawn
While night dew
Glimmered on the lawn.

"Quack! Quack!" they said.
"It's time to eat.
We'll go hunt mushrooms
For a treat."

And in the light
Of early dawn
I saw them chasing
On the lawn.

They sought their treat
With hungry quacks
And marked the dew
With criss-cross tracks.

They ate the mushrooms
One by one
And quacked to greet
The rising sun.

But in my bed
I settled back
And slept to tunes
Of "Quack! Quack! Quack!"
                    —*James S. Tippett*

PLAYMATES

And whether I went to the North Pole,
Or whether I went to the South Pole,
It would be all the same to him.

Rose Fyleman.

IF ONLY . . .

If only I'd some money,
  I'd buy a jolly boat
And get a pair of sea boots
  And a furry sort of coat,
A case or two of salted beef
  And a seaman's wooden chest,
And I'd sail away to the North Pole,
Or I'd sail away to the South Pole,
  Whichever I thought was best.

I'd get up very early—
  They wouldn't see me go—
Jimmy would be with me
  But no one else would know.
Dogs are very useful,
  And I couldn't part with Jim,
And whether I went to the North Pole,
Or whether I went to the South Pole,
  It would be all the same to him.

Perhaps we'd see a mountain
  That no one else had seen;
Perhaps we'd find a country
  Where no one else had been.
Suppose we climbed an iceberg
  And saw the midnight sun! . . .
Oh, whether we went to the North Pole,
Or whether we went to the South Pole,
  WOULDN'T it all be fun?
                    —*Rose Fyleman*

[69]

MY AIREDALE DOG

I have a funny Airedale dog,
   He's just about my size,
With such a serious-looking face,
   And eyes that seem so wise.

He looks as if he'd like to laugh,
   But yet his long, straight muzzle
Gives him a kind of solemn look—
   He surely is a puzzle.

And he is just as full of tricks
   As any dog could be,
And we have mighty jolly times
   Because he plays with me,

And never tries to bite or snap;
   He doesn't even whine,—
And that is why my Airedale dog
   Is such a friend of mine.
              —*W. L. Mason*

THE HAIRY DOG

My dog's so furry I've not seen
His face for years and years:
His eyes are buried out of sight,
I only guess his ears.

When people ask me for his breed,
I do not know or care:
He has the beauty of them all
Hidden beneath his hair.
              —*Herbert Asquith*

BINGO HAS AN ENEMY

Bingo is kind and friendly,
  A gentleman right to the core,
But he can't bear rats
And he hates all cats
  And the fuzzy brown dog next door.

There's a nice little girl who lives there,
  But they glare at us more and more;
So we never can call,
And the cause of it all
  Is the fuzzy brown dog next door.

Bingo is limping a little
  And one of his ears is sore,
He's rather a fright,
But, oh, what a sight
  Is the fuzzy brown dog next door!
                              —*Rose Fyleman*

MY DOG

I have no dog, but it must be
Somewhere there's one belongs to me—
A little chap with wagging tail,
And dark brown eyes that never quail,
But look you through, and through, and through,
With love unspeakable, but true.

Somewhere it must be, I opine,
There is a little dog of mine
With cold black nose that sniffs around
In search of what things may be found
In pocket, or some nook hard by
Where I have hid them from his eye.

Somewhere my doggie pulls and tugs
The fringes of rebellious rugs,
Or with the mischief of the pup
Chews all my shoes and slippers up,
And when he's done it to the core
With eyes all eager pleads for more.

Somewhere upon his hinder legs
My little doggie sits and begs,
And in a wistful minor tone
Pleads for the pleasures of the bone—
I pray it be his owner's whim
To yield, and grant the same to him.

Somewhere a little dog doth wait,
It may be by some garden-gate,
With eyes alert and tail attent—
You know the kind of tail that's meant—
With stores of yelps of glad delight
To bid me welcome home at night.

Somewhere a little dog is seen,
His nose two shaggy paws between,
Flat on his stomach, one eye shut
Held fast in dreamy slumber, but
The other open, ready for
His master coming through the door.

                              —*John Kendrick Bangs*

CAT

My cat
Is quiet.
She moves without a sound.
Sometimes she stretches herself high and curving
On tiptoe.
Sometimes she crouches low
And creeping.

Sometimes she rubs herself against a chair,
And there
    With a *miew* and a *miew*
    And a purrrr purrrr purrrr
    She curls up
    And goes to sleep.

My cat
Lives through a black hole
Under the house.
So one day I
Crawled in after her.
And it was dark
And I sat
And didn't know
Where to go.
And then—
Two yellow-white
Round little lights
Came moving . . . moving . . . toward me.
And there
With a *miew* and a *miew*
And a purrrr purrrr purrrr
My cat
Rubbed, soft, against me.

And I knew
The lights
WERE MY CAT'S EYES
In the dark.
               —*Dorothy W. Baruch*

A DIRGE FOR A RIGHTEOUS KITTEN

Ding-dong, ding-dong, ding-dong.
Here lies a kitten good, who kept
A kitten's proper place.
He stole no pantry eatables,
Nor scratched the baby's face.
He let the alley-cats alone.
He had no yowling voice.
His shirt was always laundried well,
He freed the house of mice.
Until his death he had not caused
His little mistress tears,
He wore his ribbon prettily,
He washed behind his ears.
Ding-dong, ding-dong, ding-dong.
               —*Vachel Lindsay*

THE LOOKING-GLASS PUSSY

(The Kitten Speaks)

Back behind the mirror is another pussy-cat
With bows and whiskers just like mine, and just as gray and
    fat.

She peeps around and looks at me when I peep in at her,
And looks as pleased as possible each time she hears me purr.

She pats her paws against the glass when I pat mine there
    too;
But she won't come and play with me, no matter how I mew!

One day I thought I'd catch her when I didn't see her there;
(She couldn't see me either—I was down behind a chair!)

I crept behind the furniture and slid along the wall
And ran behind the mirror—and she wasn't there at all!

But when I bounced around the frame as sudden as could be
That tricky little cat was there a-looking out at me!
—Margaret Widdemer

CAT

The black cat yawns,
Opens her jaws,
Stretches her legs,
And shows her claws.

Then she gets up
And stands on four
Long stiff legs
And yawns some more.

She shows her sharp teeth,
She stretches her lip,
Her slice of a tongue
Turns up at the tip.

Lifting herself
On her delicate toes,
She arches her back
As high as it goes.

She lets herself down
With particular care,
And pads away
With her tail in the air.
                —*Mary Britton Miller*

THE MYSTERIOUS CAT

I saw a proud, mysterious cat,
I saw a proud, mysterious cat,
Too proud to catch a mouse or rat—
Mew, mew, mew.

But catnip she would eat, and purr,
But catnip she would eat, and purr.
And goldfish she did much prefer—
Mew, mew, mew.

I saw a cat—'twas but a dream,
I saw a cat—'twas but a dream,
Who scorned the slave that brought her cream—
Mew, mew, mew.

Unless the slave were dressed in style,
Unless the slave were dressed in style,
And knelt before her all the while—
Mew, mew, mew.

Did you ever hear of a thing like that?
Did you ever hear of a thing like that?
Did you ever hear of a thing like that?
Oh, what a proud mysterious cat.
Oh, what a proud mysterious cat.
Oh, what a proud mysterious cat.
Mew. . . . mew. . . . mew.

—*Vachel Lindsay*

RABBITS

My two white rabbits
Chase each other
With humping, bumping backs.
   They go hopping, hopping,
   And their long ears
     Go flopping, flopping.
      And they
      Make faces
      With their noses
      Up and down.

Today
I went inside their fence
To play rabbit with them.
And in one corner
Under a loose bush
I saw something shivering the leaves.
And I pushed
And looked.
And I found—
There
In a hole
In the ground—
Three baby rabbits
Hidden away.
      And *they*
      Made faces
      With their noses
      Up and down.
           —*Dorothy W. Baruch*

THE LITTLE TURTLE

There was a little turtle.
He lived in a box.
He swam in a puddle.
He climbed on the rocks.

He snapped at a mosquito.
He snapped at a flea.
He snapped at a minnow.
And he snapped at me.

He caught the mosquito.
He caught the flea.
He caught the minnow.
But he didn't catch me.
                    —*Vachel Lindsay*

ABOUT ANIMALS

Animals are my friends and my kin and my playfellows;
They love me as I love them.
I have a feeling for them I cannot express . . .
It burns in my heart.
I make thoughts about them to keep in my mind.
I warm the cold, help the hurt, play with the frolicsome;
I laugh to see two puppies playing
And I wonder which is which!
General is a dog with blue-black eyes;
They shine . . . there is a love comes from them;
He is filled with joy when he guards me;
His eyes try to speak.
I see his mind through them
When he asks me to say things for him as well as I can
Because he has no words.
                    —*Hilda Conkling*

A BOY AND A PUP

The boy wears a grin,
A scratch on his chin,
A wind-rumpled thatch,
A visible patch,
A cheek like a rose,
A frecklesome nose.

The pup, though he may
Be tawny as hay,
Is blithe as a song;
He gambols along
And waves to each friend
A wagglesome end.

With whistle and bark
They're off for a lark;
According to whim,
A hunt or a swim,
A tramp or a run
Or any old fun.

They don't care a jot
If school keeps or not,
When anything's up,
The boy and the pup—
That duo of joy,
A pup and a boy!
                    —*Arthur Guiterman*

FEATHERED FRIENDS.

Feathered birds in the rain sweet sky,
At their ease in the air, flit low, flit high.

Walter de la Mare.

TIME TO RISE

A birdie with a yellow bill
Hopped upon the window sill,
Cocked his shining eye and said:
"Ain't you 'shamed, you sleepy-head!"
                    —*Robert Louis Stevenson*

THE WOODPECKER

The woodpecker pecked out a little round hole
And made him a house in the telephone pole.

One day when I watched he poked out his head,
And he had on a hood and a collar of red.

When the streams of rain pour out of the sky,
And the sparkles of lightning go flashing by,

And the big, big wheels of thunder roll,
He can snuggle back in the telephone pole.
                    —*Elizabeth Madox Roberts*

THE WOODPECKER

The wizard of the woods is he;
    For in his daily round,
Where'er he finds a rotting tree,
    He makes the timber sound.
                    —*John Banister Tabb*

THE SNOW-BIRD

When all the ground with snow is white,
    The merry snow-bird comes,
And hops about with great delight
    To find the scattered crumbs.

How glad he seems to get to eat
    A piece of cake or bread!
He wears no shoes upon his feet,
    Nor hat upon his head.

But happiest is he, I know,
    Because no cage with bars
Keeps him from walking on the snow
    And printing it with stars.
          —Frank Dempster Sherman

THE SECRET

We have a secret, just we three,
The robin, and I, and the sweet cherry-tree;
The bird told the tree, and the tree told me,
And nobody knows it but just us three.

But of course the robin knows it best,
Because he built the—I shan't tell the rest;
And laid the four little—something in it—
I'm afraid I shall tell it every minute.

But if the tree and the robin don't peep,
I'll try my best the secret to keep;
Though I know when the little birds fly about
Then the whole secret will be out.
          —Author Unknown

ROBIN REDBREAST

A Child's Song

Good-bye, good-bye to Summer!
  For Summer's nearly done;
The garden smiling faintly,
  Cool breezes in the sun;
Our Thrushes now are silent,
  Our Swallows flown away—
But Robin's here, in coat of brown,
  With ruddy breast-knot gay.
Robin, Robin Redbreast,
  O Robin dear!
Robin singing sweetly
  In the falling of the year.

Bright yellow, red, and orange,
  The leaves come down in hosts;
The trees are Indian Princes,
  But soon they'll turn to Ghosts;
The scanty pears and apples
  Hang russet on the bough,
It's Autumn, Autumn, Autumn late,
  'Twill soon be Winter now.
Robin, Robin Redbreast,
  O Robin dear!
And welaway! my Robin,
  For pinching times are near.

The fireside for the Cricket,
The wheatstack for the Mouse,
When trembling night-winds whistle
And moan all round the house;
The frosty ways like iron,
The branches plumed with snow—
Alas! in Winter, dead and dark,
Where can poor Robin go?
Robin, Robin Redbreast,
O Robin dear!
And a crumb of bread for Robin,
His little heart to cheer.
—William Allingham

THE OWL

When cats run home and light is come,
And dew is cold upon the ground,
And the far-off stream is dumb,
And the whirring sail goes round,
And the whirring sail goes round;
Alone and warming his five wits,
The white owl in the belfry sits.

When merry milkmaids click the latch,
And rarely smells the new-mown hay,
And the cock hath sung beneath the thatch
Twice or thrice his roundelay,
Twice or thrice his roundelay;
Alone and warming his five wits,
The white owl in the belfry sits.
—Alfred Tennyson

THE EAGLE

Fragment

He clasps the crag with crooked hands;
Close to the sun in lonely lands,
Ring'd with the azure world, he stands,

The wrinkled sea beneath him crawls;
He watches from his mountain walls,
And like a thunderbolt he falls.
—Alfred Tennyson

THE SANDPIPER

Across the narrow beach we flit,
    One little sandpiper and I;
And fast I gather, bit by bit,
    The scattered driftwood bleached and dry.
The wild waves reach their hands for it,
    The wild wind raves, the tide runs high,
As up and down the beach we flit,
    One little sandpiper and I.

Above our heads the sullen clouds
    Scud black and swift across the sky;
Like silent ghosts in misty shrouds
    Stand out the white light-houses high.
Almost as far as eye can reach
    I see the close-reefed vessels fly,
As fast we flit along the beach,
    One little sandpiper and I.

[87]

I watch him as he skims along
  Uttering his sweet and mournful cry;
He starts not at my fitful song,
  Or flash of fluttering drapery.
He has no thought of any wrong;
  He scans me with a fearless eye.
Stanch friends are we, well tried and strong,
  The little sandpiper and I.

Comrade, where wilt thou be tonight
  When the loosed storm breaks furiously?
My driftwood fire will burn so bright!
  To what warm shelter canst thou fly?
I do not fear for thee, though wroth
  The tempest rushes through the sky:
For are we not God's children both,
  Thou, little sandpiper, and I?
                    —*Celia Thaxter*

THE SEA GULL

I watched the pretty, white sea gull
Come riding into town;
The waves came up when he came up,
Went down when he went down.
                    —*Leroy F. Jackson*

[88]

SINGING WINGS

When God had made a host of them,
One little flower still lacked a stem
    To hold its blossom blue;
So into it He breathed a song,
And suddenly, with petals strong
    As wings, away it flew.

                John Banister Tabb.

BE LIKE THE BIRD

Be like the bird, who
Halting in his flight
On limb too slight
Feels it give way beneath him,
Yet sings
Knowing he hath wings.
                    —*Victor Hugo*

THE BLACKBIRD

In the far corner
close by the swings,
every morning
a blackbird sings.

His bill's so yellow,
his coat's so black,
that he makes a fellow
whistle back.

Ann, my daughter,
thinks that he
sings for us two
especially.
                    —*Humbert Wolfe*

[91]

THE RIVALS

I heard a bird at dawn
Singing sweetly on a tree,
That the dew was on the lawn,
And the wind was on the lea;
But I didn't listen to him,
For he didn't sing to me.

I didn't listen to him,
For he didn't sing to me
That the dew was on the lawn
And the wind was on the lea!
I was singing at the time,
Just as prettily as he!

I was singing all the time,
Just as prettily as he,
About the dew upon the lawn,
And the wind upon the lea!
So I didn't listen to him,
As he sang upon a tree!

—*James Stephens*

RED-TOP AND TIMOTHY

Red-Top and Timothy
  Come here in the spring;
Light spears out of emerald sheaths
  Everywhere they swing.
Harmless little soldiers,
  On the field they play,
Nodding plumes and crossing blades
  All the livelong day.

Timothy and Red-Top
    Bring their music-band;
Some with scarlet epaulettes
    Strutting stiff and grand;
Some in sky-blue jackets;
    Some in vests of pink:
Red and white their leader's coat,
    Restless Bob-o'-link!

Red-Top's airy feathers
    Tremble to his notes,
In themselves an orchestra;
    Then a thousand throats
Set the winds a-laughing,
    While the saucy thing
Anywhere, on spike or spear,
    Sways himself to sing.

Red-Top and Timothy
    Have a mortal foe;
There's a giant with a scythe
    Comes and lays them low;
Shuts them in barn-prisons;
    Spares not even Sweet Clover:
Bob-o'-link leads off his band,
    Now the campaign's over.

                        —*Lucy Larcom*

WHY READ A BOOK?

Why read a book when there are birds
Printing clear and breezy words
Upon the clouds' white pages? When
A busy robin and a wren
Are syllables of ecstasy?
A line of swallows on a tree,
Or wire, is a sentence, long
And sweeping. A flying flock's a strong
Paragraph, while in the air
Is quilled elaborately a rare
Illumined manuscript in gold
And green. And say what book can hold
More fascination and delight
Than birds in migratory flight?

—*Colette M. Burns*

ANSWER TO A CHILD'S QUESTION

Do you ask what the birds say? The sparrow, the dove,
The linnet, and thrush say, "I love and I love!"
In the winter they're silent—the wind is so strong;
What it says, I don't know, but it sings a loud song.
But green leaves and blossoms, and sunny warm weather,
And singing, and loving—all come back together.
But the lark is so brimful of gladness and love,
The green fields below him, the blue sky above,
That he sings, and he sings; and forever sings he—
"I love my Love, and my Love loves me!"

—*Samuel Taylor Coleridge*

WILD GEESE

The wind blows, the sun shines, the birds sing loud,
The blue, blue sky is flecked with fleecy dappled cloud,
Over earth's rejoicing fields the children dance and sing,
And the frogs pipe in chorus, "It is spring! It is spring!"

The grass comes, the flower laughs where lately lay the
    snow,
O'er the breezy hill-top hoarsely calls the crow,
By the flowing river the alder catkins swing,
And the sweet song sparrow cries, "Spring! It is spring!"

Hark, what a clamor goes winging through the sky!
Look, children! Listen to the sound so wild and high!
Like a peal of broken bells,—kling, klang, kling,—
Far and high the wild geese cry, "Spring! It is spring!"

Bear the winter off with you, O wild geese dear!
Carry all the cold away, far away from here;
Chase the snow into the north, O strong of heart and wing,
While we share the robin's rapture, crying, "Spring! It is
    spring!"

—*Celia Thaxter*

JESTER BEE

The garden is a royal court
   Whose jester is the bee,
And with his wit and merry sport
   He fills the place with glee.

He sings love ditties to the Rose
   Who is the queen of all;
To princess Lily up he goes
   And whispers she is tall.

He pulls prince Pansy by the ear;
   He does all sorts of things
That are ridiculous and queer—
   But all the while he sings.

He does not seem to think it wrong
   Such liberties to take;
And they who love his happy song
   Forgive him for its sake.

And when at last the royal clown
   Takes off his jester's mask,
He seriously sits him down
   Before his honey task.

Then to himself he sings away,
   And here's the burden true:
"Oh, sweet are all my hours of play,
   And sweet my honey, too!"
       —*Frank Dempster Sherman*

FRAIL WINGS

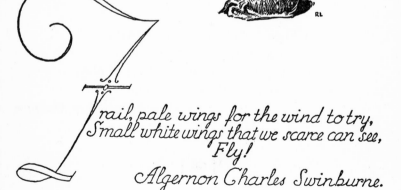

Frail, pale wings for the wind to try,
Small white wings that we scarce can see,
Fly!

Algernon Charles Swinburne.

WHITE BUTTERFLIES

Fly, white butterflies, out to sea,
Frail, pale wings for the wind to try,
Small white wings that we scarce can see,
    Fly!

Some fly light as a laugh of glee,
Some fly soft as a long, low sigh;
All to the haven where each would be,
    Fly!
           —Algernon Charles Swinburne

BUTTERFLY

Butterfly, Butterfly, sipping the sand,
Have you forgotten the flowers of the land?
Or are you so sated with honey and dew
That sand-filtered water tastes better to you?
           —John Banister Tabb

FLIES

Flies walk on ceilings
And straight up the walls
Not even the littlest
Fly ever falls.

And I am quite certain
If *I* were a fly
I'd leave my home and go
Walk on the sky.
         —Dorothy Aldis

GREEN MOTH

The night the green moth came for me,
   A creamy moon poured down the hill,
The meadow seemed a silver sea,
Small pearls were hung in every tree,
   And all so still, so still.

He floated in on my white bed,
   A strange and soundless fellow.
I saw the horns wave on his head,
   He stepped across my pillow
In tiny ermine boots, and spread
   His cape of green and yellow.

He came so close that I could see
   His golden eyes, and sweet and chill,
His faint breath wavered over me.
"Come Child, my Beautiful," said he,
   And all so still, so still.
                —*Winifred Welles*

MOTH MILLER

The timid little night moth
That hovers near our light
Has silver dust upon his wings
And tiny flecks of white,

And if you would look closely
There's flour upon his clothes:
But *that* is just because he is
A miller . . . I suppose.
                —*Aileen Fisher*

A BEE SETS SAIL

The wind blows east, the wind blows storm,
And yet this very hour
I saw a bumblebee embark
In frigate of a flower;

An admiral in epaulets,
He strode the scented deck
And in the teeth of tossing gales
He rode without a wreck.

More valorous adventurer
I never hope to see,—
Though mariners be gallant men,—
Than that same bumblebee.

—*Katharine Morse*

THE TAX-GATHERER

"And pray, who are you?"
Said the violet blue
To the Bee, with surprise
At his wonderful size,
In her eye-glass of dew.

"I, Madam," quoth he,
"Am a publican Bee,
Collecting the tax
On honey and wax.
Have you nothing for me?"

—*John Banister Tabb*

FIREFLY

A Song

A little light is going by,
Is going up to see the sky,
A little light with wings.

I never could have thought of it,
To have a little bug all lit
And made to go on wings.

—Elizabeth Madox Roberts

FIREFLIES

Little lamps of the dusk,
    You fly low and gold
When the summer evening
    Starts to unfold
So that all the insects,
    Now, before you pass,
Will have light to see by
    Undressing in the grass.

But when night has flowered,
    Little lamps agleam,
You fly over treetops
    Following a dream.
Men wonder from their windows
    That a firefly goes so far—
They do not know your longing
    To be a shooting star.

—Carolyn Hall

FIREFLIES

I like to chase the fireflies,
    Chase them to and fro;
I like to watch them dart about,
    Their little lamps aglow.

In the evening's twilight dim
    I follow them about;
I often think I have one caught,
    And then his light goes out.

I cannot tell just where he is
    Until he winks, you see,
Then far away I see his light,
    He's played a joke on me.
                    —*Grace Wilson Coplen*

THE FIRE-FLY

"Are you flying through the night
    Looking where to find me?"
"Nay, I travel with a light
    For the folks *behind* me."
                    —*John Banister Tabb*

THE HUMBLE BUMBLE BEE

The weather-man has promised snow and sleet.
Now bumble bee where will you warm your feet?
"Beside the Sangamon a hollow oak
Has been my winter wigwam; 'tis the cloak
That shields the Indian fairies and their king:
They sleep on mouse-hides in a rainbow ring
Of bees in war-paint, crouched in thick array
Who scare the cut-worms and the ants away.
I lead those braves, commanding them to kneel
And buzz, as on their wings I put my heel.
In winter, fairyland belongs to me.
In summer I'm a humble bumble bee."
                                        —*Vachel Lindsay*

LITTLE FOLKS
IN THE GRASS

In the grass
A thousand little people pass.
Annette Wynne.

LITTLE FOLKS IN THE GRASS

In the grass
A thousand little people pass,
And all about a myriad little eyes look out,
For there are houses every side
Where the little folks abide,
Where the little folks take tea
On a grass blade near a tree;
Where they hold their Sabbath meetings,
Pass each other, giving greetings,
So remember when you pass
Through the grass;
Little folks are everywhere;
Walk quite softly, take great care
Lest you hurt them unaware,
Lest the giant that is you
Pull a house down with his shoe,
Pull a house down, roof and all,
Killing children, great and small;
So the wee eyes look at you
As you walk the meadows through,
So remember when you pass
Through the grass!

—*Annette Wynne*

GRASSHOPPER GREEN

Grasshopper green is a comical chap;
    He lives on the best of fare.
Bright little trousers, jacket, and cap,
    These are his summer wear.

[107]

Out in the meadow he loves to go,
    Playing away in the sun;
It's hopperty, skipperty, high and low,
    Summer's the time for fun.

Grasshopper green has a quaint little house;
    It's under the hedge so gay.
Grandmother Spider, as still as a mouse,
    Watches him over the way.
Gladly he's calling the children, I know,
    Out in the beautiful sun;
It's hopperty, skipperty, high and low,
    Summer's the time for fun.

                              —*Author Unknown*

THE GRASSHOPPERS

High
Up
Over the top
Of feathery grasses the
Grasshoppers hop.
They won't eat their suppers;
They will not obey
Their grasshopper mothers
And fathers, who say:
"Listen, my children,
This must be stopped—
Now is the time your last
Hop should be hopped;
So come eat your suppers
And go to your beds—"
But the little green grasshoppers
Shake their green heads.

"No,
No—"
The naughty ones say,
"All we have time to do
Now is to play.
If we want supper we'll
Nip at a fly
Or nibble a blueberry
As we go by;
If we feel sleepy we'll
Close our eyes tight
And snoozle away in a
Harebell all night.
But not
Now.
Now we must hop.
And nobody,
Nobody,
Can make us stop."
—*Dorothy Aldis*

SPLINTER

The voice of the last cricket
across the first frost
is one kind of good-by.
It is so thin a splinter of singing.
—*Carl Sandburg*

BROWN AND FURRY

Brown and furry
Caterpillar in a hurry
Take your walk
To the shady leaf, or stalk,
Or what not,
Which may be the chosen spot.
No toad spy you,
Hovering bird of prey pass by you;
Spin and die,
To live again a butterfly.
　　　　　　　　—Christina G. Rossetti

THE TIRED CATERPILLAR

A tired caterpillar went to sleep one day
In a snug little cradle of silken gray.
And he said, as he softly curled up in his nest,
"Oh, crawling was pleasant, but rest is best."

He slept through the winter long and cold,
All tightly up in his blanket rolled,
And at last he awoke on a warm spring day
To find that winter had gone away.

He awoke to find he had golden wings,
And no longer need crawl over sticks and things.
"Oh, the earth is nice," said the glad butterfly,
"But the sky is best, when we learn to fly!"
　　　　　　　　—Author Unknown

IN THE GARDEN

Come!' said Old Shellover.
'What?' says Creep.
The horny old Gardener's fast asleep';
Walter de la Mare.

OLD SHELLOVER

"Come!" said Old Shellover.
"What?" says Creep.
"The horny old Gardener's fast asleep;
The fat cock Thrush
To his nest has gone,
And the dew shines bright
In the rising Moon;
Old Sallie Worm from her hole doth peep;
Come!" said Old Shellover,
"Ah!" said Creep.

—Walter de la Mare

LITTLE SNAIL

I saw a little snail
Come down the garden walk.
He wagged his head this way . . . that way . . .
Like a clown in a circus.
He looked from side to side
As though he were from a different country.
I have always said he carries his house on his back . . .
To-day in the rain
I saw that it was his umbrella!

—Hilda Conkling

THE SNAIL

The snail is very odd and slow.
He has his mind made up to go
The longest way to anywhere
And will not let you steer him there.

Today I met one in the grass
And hadn't time to watch him pass,
But coming back at sunset, I
Discovered him still traveling by.

The grass-blades grew so thick and tall
I asked him why he climbed them all,
And told him I had sometimes found
The shortest way was going 'round.

He was not easy to persuade,
To judge by any sign he made,
And when I lectured him some more
Went in his house and shut the door.
                    —*Grace Hazard Conkling*

THE SNAIL'S DREAM

A snail who had a way, it seems,
Of dreaming very curious dreams,
Once dream't he was—you'll never guess!—
The Lightning Limited Express!
                    —*Oliver Herford*

A FRIEND IN THE GARDEN

He is not John the gardener,
  And yet the whole day long
Employs himself most usefully
  The flower-beds among.

He is not Tom the pussy-cat;
  And yet the other day,
With stealthy stride and glistening eye,
  He crept upon his prey.

He is not Dash, the dear old dog,
  And yet, perhaps, if you
Took pains with him and petted him,
  You'd come to love him too.

He's not a blackbird, though he chirps.
  And though he once was black;
And now he wears a loose, grey coat,
  All wrinkled on the back.

He's got a very dirty face,
  And very shining eyes!
He sometimes comes and sits indoors;
  He looks—and p'r'aps is—wise.

But in a sunny flower-bed
  He has his fixed abode;
He eats the things that eat my plants—
  He is a friendly TOAD.
                    —*Juliana Horatia Ewing*

THE WORM

Dickie found a broken spade
And said he'd dig himself a well;
And then Charles took a piece of tin,
And I was digging with a shell.

Then Will said he would dig one too.
We shaped them out and made them wide,
And I dug up a piece of clod
That had a little worm inside.

We watched him pucker up himself
And stretch himself to walk away.
He tried to go inside the dirt,
But Dickie made him wait and stay.

His shining skin was soft and wet.
I poked him once to see him squirm.
And then Will said, "I wonder if
He knows that he's a worm."

And then we sat back on our feet
And wondered for a little bit.
And we forgot to dig our wells
A while, and tried to answer it.

And while we tried to find it out,
He puckered in a little wad,
And then he stretched himself again
And went back home inside the clod.

     —*Elizabeth Madox Roberts*

THE WORM

When the earth is turned in spring
The worms are fat as anything.

And birds come flying all around
To eat the worms right off the ground.

They like worms just as much as I
Like bread and milk and apple pie.

And once, when I was very young,
I put a worm right on my tongue.

I didn't like the taste a bit,
And so I didn't swallow it.

But oh, it makes my Mother squirm
Because she *thinks* I ate that worm!

—Ralph Bergengren

A BIRD

A bird came down the walk:
He did not know I saw;
He bit an angle-worm in halves
And ate the fellow, raw.

And then he drank a dew
From a convenient grass,
And then hopped sidewise to the wall
To let a beetle pass.
                              —*Emily Dickinson*

LITTLE FURRY CREATURES

He sat down close where I could see,
And his big still eyes looked hard at me.
Elizabeth Madox Roberts.

THE RABBIT

When they said the time to hide was mine,
I hid back under a thick grape vine.

And while I was still for the time to pass,
A little gray thing came out of the grass.

He hopped his way through the melon bed
And sat down close by a cabbage head.

He sat down close where I could see,
And his big still eyes looked hard at me,

His big eyes bursting out of the rim,
And I looked back very hard at him.
                    —*Elizabeth Madox Roberts*

LITTLE CHARLIE CHIPMUNK

Little Charlie Chipmunk was a *talker*. Mercy me!
He chattered after breakfast and he chattered after tea!
He chattered to his father and he chattered to his mother!
He chattered to his sister and he chattered to his brother!
He chattered till his family was almost driven *wild*
Oh, little Charlie Chipmunk was a *very* tiresome child!
                    —*Helen Cowles Lecron*

THE SQUIRREL

Whisky, frisky,
Hippity hop,
Up he goes
To the tree top!

Whirly, twirly,
Round and round,
Down he scampers
To the ground.

Furly, curly
What a tail!
Tall as a feather
Broad as a sail!

Where's his supper?
In the shell,
Snappity, crackity,
Out it fell!

—Author Unknown

FABLE

The mountain and the squirrel
Had a quarrel,
And the former called the latter, "Little Prig";
Bun replied,
"You are doubtless very big;
But all sorts of things and weather
Must be taken in together,
To make up a year
And a sphere.
And I think it no disgrace
To occupy my place.
If I'm not so large as you,
You are not so small as I,
And not half so spry.
I'll not deny you make
A very pretty squirrel track;
Talents differ; all is well and wisely put;
If I cannot carry forests on my back,
Neither can you crack a nut."

—Ralph Waldo Emerson

FIVE EYES

In Hans' old Mill his three black cats
Watch the bins for the thieving rats.
Whisker and claw, they crouch in the night,
Their five eyes smouldering green and bright:
Squeaks from the flour sacks, squeaks from where
The cold wind stirs on the empty stair,
Squeaking and scampering, everywhere.
Then down they pounce, now in, now out,
At whisking tail, and sniffing snout;
While lean old Hans he snores away
Till peep of light at break of day;
Then up he climbs to his creaking mill,
Out come his cats all grey with meal—
Jekkel, and Jessup, and one-eyed Jill.
                              —*Walter de la Mare*

A CHINESE NURSERY RHYME

He ran up the candlestick,
    The little mousey brown,
To steal and eat tallow,
    And he couldn't get down.
He called for his grandma,
    But his grandma was in town;
So he doubled up into a wheel
    And rolled himself down.
                    —*Trans. by I. T. Headland*

THE MOUSE

I heard a mouse
Bitterly complaining
In a crack of moonlight
Aslant on the floor—

"Little I ask
And that little is not granted.
There are few crumbs
In this world any more.

"The bread-box is tin
And I cannot get in.

"The jam's in a jar
My teeth cannot mar.

"The cheese sits by itself
On the pantry shelf—

"All night I run
Searching and seeking,
All night I run
About on the floor.

"Moonlight is there
And a bare place for dancing,
But no little feast
Is spread any more."
                    —*Elizabeth Coatsworth*

THE CITY MOUSE AND THE GARDEN MOUSE

The city mouse lives in a house;—
The garden mouse lives in a bower,
He's friendly with the frogs and toads,
And sees the pretty plants in flower.

The city mouse eats bread and cheese;—
The garden mouse eats what he can;
We will not grudge him seeds and stalks,
Poor little timid furry man.

—Christina G. Rossetti

ON FOURS

Low on his fours the Lion
Treads with the surly Bear;
Walter de la Mare.

UNSTOOPING

Low on his fours the Lion
   Treads with the surly Bear;
But Men straight upward from the dust
   Walk with their heads in air;
The free sweet winds of heaven,
   The sunlight from on high
Beat on their clear bright cheeks and brows
   As they go striding by;
The doors of all their houses
   They arch so they may go,
Uplifted o'er the four-feet beasts,
   Unstooping, to and fro.
                    —*Walter de la Mare*

I WONDER IF THE LION KNOWS

I wonder if the lion knows
   That people are afraid
To meet him when for walks he goes
   Beneath the jungle shade;
And when they scream and run away,
O, does he laugh at their dismay?
And does he say with head tossed high:
"How 'terribully' fierce am I"?

I'd like to know
If this is so;
But if I met a lion some day
I would not ask, I'd run away,
For surely it is not a treat
To meet a lion on the street!
                    —*Annette Wynne*

THE BROWN BEAR

Now the wild bees that hive in the rocks
Are winding their horns, elfin shrill,
And hark, at the pine tree the woodpecker knocks,
And the speckled grouse pipes on the hill.
Now the adder's dull brood wakes to run,
Now the sap mounts abundant and good,
And the brown bear has turned with his side to the sun
In his lair in the depth of the wood—
Old Honey-Paw wakes in the wood.

"Oh, a little more slumber," says he,
"And a little more turning to sleep,"
But he feels the spring fervor that hurries the bee
And the hunger that makes the trout leap;
So he ambles by thicket and trail,
So he noses the tender young shoots,
In the spring of year at the sign of the quail
The brown bear goes digging for roots—
For sappy and succulent roots.

Oh, as still goes the wolf on his quest
As the spotted snake glides through the rocks,
And the deer and the sheep count the lightest foot best,
And slinking and sly trots the fox.
But fleet-foot and light-foot will stay,
And fawns by their mothers will quail
At the saplings that snap and the thickets that sway
When Honey-Paw takes to the trail—
When he shuffles and grunts on the trail.

He has gathered the ground squirrel's hoard,
He has rifled the store of the bees,
He has caught the young trout at the shoals of the ford
And stripped the wild plums from the trees;
So robbing and ranging he goes,
And the right to his pillage makes good
Till he rounds out the year at the first of the snows
In his lair in the depth of the wood—
Old Honey-Paw sleeps in the wood.

—*Mary Austin*

THE WOLF

When the pale moon hides and the wild wind wails,
And over the tree-tops the nighthawk sails,
The gray wolf sits on the world's far rim,
And howls: and it seems to comfort him.

The wolf is a lonely soul, you see,
No beast in the wood, nor bird in the tree,
But shuns his path; in the windy gloom
They give him plenty, and plenty of room.

So he sits with his long, lean face to the sky
Watching the ragged clouds go by.
There in the night, alone, apart,
Singing the song of his lone, wild heart.

Far away, on the world's dark rim
He howls, and it seems to comfort him.

—*Georgia Roberts Durston*

THERE ARE NO WOLVES IN ENGLAND NOW

There are no wolves in England now, nor any grizzly bears;
You could not meet them after dark upon the attic stairs.

When Nanna goes to fetch the tea there is no need at all
To leave the nursery door ajar in case you want to call.

And mother says, in fairy tales, those bits are never true
That tell you all the dreadful deeds that wicked fairies do.

And wouldn't it be silly for a great big girl like me
To be the leastest bit afraid of things that couldn't be?

—Rose Fyleman

THE WOLVES

When Grandmother Polly had married and gone,
But before her father had given her Clem,
Or Joe, or Sandy, or Evaline—
Before he had given her any of *them,*

She used to live in a far-away place,
In a little cabin that was her home,
And all around were bushes and trees,
And the wolves could come.

At night they ran down out of the rocks
And bristled up their trembly fur.
They came and howled by Polly's door
And showed their little white teeth at her.

—Elizabeth Madox Roberts

THE HIPPOPOTAMUS

In the squdgy river,
  Down the oozely bank,
Where the ripples shiver,
  And the reeds are rank.

Where the purple Kippo
  Makes an awful fuss,
Lives the hip-hip-hippo
  Hippo-pot-a-mus!

Broad his back and steady;
  Broad and flat his nose;
Sharp and keen and ready
  Little eyes are those.

You would think him dreaming
  Where the mud is deep.
It is only seeming—
  He is not asleep.

Better not disturb him,
  There'd be an awful fuss
If you touched the Hippo,
  Hippo-pot-a-mus.
                —*Georgia Roberts Durston*

LONE DOG

I'm a lean dog, a keen dog, a wild dog, and lone;
I'm a rough dog, a tough dog, hunting on my own;
I'm a bad dog, a mad dog, teasing silly sheep;
I love to sit and bay the moon, to keep fat souls from sleep.

I'll never be a lap dog, licking dirty feet,
A sleek dog, a meek dog, cringing for my meat,
Not for me the fireside, the well-filled plate,
But shut door, and sharp stone, and cuff and kick and hate.

Not for me the other dogs, running by my side,
Some have run a short while, but none of them would bide.
O mine is still the lone trail, the hard trail, the best,
Wide wind, the wild stars, and hunger of the quest!

—Irene Rutherford McLeod

ANIMAL FANCIES

The rain, they say, is a mouse-gray horse
That is shod with a silver shoe;
The sound of his hoofs can be heard on the roofs
As he gallops the whole night through.

Rowena Bastin Bennett.

UNDER THE TENT OF THE SKY

The wind cracked his whip,
The storm flashed a gun,
And the animal-clouds marched one by one
Under the tent of the sky.

There were elephants, blue,
And shaggy white bears,
And dozens and dozens of prancing gray mares
With their beautiful heads held high.

There were soft-footed panthers
And ostriches, fluffy,
And a great hippopotamus, purple and puffy,
Who wallowed in mud-colored mist.

There were small curly dogs
And camels with humps
And a wrinkled rhinoceros, all over bumps,
With a horn as big as your fist.

There was even a lion
Bedecked with a mane
Who growled so loud that he turned into rain
And tumbled to earth with a sigh.

The wind cracked his whip
And out came the sun
And the animal-clouds passed one by one
Out of the tent of the sky.

—Rowena Bastin Bennett

[137]

WIND-WOLVES

Do you hear the cry as the pack goes by,
The wind-wolves hunting across the sky?
Hear them tongue it, keen and clear,
Hot on the flanks of the flying deer!

Across the forest, mere, and plain,
Their hunting howl goes up again!
All night they'll follow the ghostly trail,
All night we'll hear their phantom wail,

For tonight the wind-wolf pack holds sway
From Pegasus Square to the Milky Way,
And the frightened bands of cloud-deer flee
In scattered groups of two and three.
                            —*William D. Sargent*

WIND IS A CAT

Wind is a cat
    That prowls at night,
Now in a valley,
    Now on a height,

Pouncing on houses
    Till folks in their beds
Draw all the covers
    Over their heads.

It sings to the moon,
    It scratches at doors;
It lashes its tail
    Around chimneys and roars.

[138]

It claws at the clouds
  Till it fringes their silk,
It laps up the dawn
  Like a saucer of milk;

Then, chasing the stars
  To the tops of the firs,
Curls down for a nap
  And purrs and purrs.
                —*Ethel Romig Fuller*

SILVER SHEEP

The sun's a bright-haired shepherd boy,
Who drives the stars away;
Beyond the far blue meadows
He shuts them up by day.

At six or seven or eight o'clock,
Over the bars they leap—
The rams with horns of silver,
The little silver sheep.

And while the shepherd takes a nap
Behind a hill, near-by,
They roam the dusky pasture
And graze upon the sky.
                —*Anne Blackwell Payne*

[139]

THE MOON-SHEEP

The moon seems like a docile sheep,
She pastures while all people sleep;
But sometimes, when she goes astray,
She wanders all alone by day.

Up in the clear blue morning air
We are surprised to see her there,
Grazing in her woolly white,
Waiting the return of night.

When dusk lets down the meadow bars
She greets again her lambs, the stars!
—Christopher Morley

THE PLEIADS

"Who are ye with clustered light,
    Little Sisters seven?"
"Crickets, chirping all the night
    On the hearth of heaven."
—John Banister Tabb

WHAT GRANDPA MOUSE SAID

The moon's a holy owl-queen.
She keeps them in a jar
Under her arm till evening,
Then sallies forth to war.

She pours the owls upon us.
They hoot with horrid noise
And eat the naughty mousie-girls
And wicked mousie-boys.

So climb the moonvine every night
And to the owl-queen pray:
Leave good green cheese by moonlit trees
For her to take away.

And never squeak, my children,
Nor gnaw the smoke-house door:
The owl-queen then will love us
And send her birds no more.

—Vachel Lindsay

WHITE HORSES

Little White Horses are out on the sea,
  Bridled with rainbows and speckled with foam,
Laden with presents for you and for me;
  Mermaids and fairies are riding them home!
      Gold from the sun;
      Diamonds rare
      Made from dew
      And frosty air;
      Veils of mist,
      Soft and white,
      Rose and silver,
      Shimmering, bright;
      Sweetest perfumes,
      Coloured shells,
      Lilting music,
      Fairy bells:
Fairies and mermaids are bringing them home
On Little White Horses all speckled with foam.
                    —*Winifred Howard*

HORSES OF THE SEA

The horses of the sea
  Rear a foaming crest,
But the horses of the land
  Serve us the best.

The horses of the land
  Munch corn and clover,
While the foaming sea-horses
  Toss and turn over.
                  —*Christina G. Rossetti*

SHELL CASTLES

A sea shell is a castle
Where a million echoes roam,
   A wee castle,
   Sea castle,
Tossed up by the foam;
   A wee creature's
   Sea creature's
Long deserted home.

If I were very tiny,
   I should walk those winding halls
And listen to the voices
   In the pink and pearly walls;
And each mysterious echo
   Would tell me salty tales
Of the phosphorescent fishes
And the white-winged ship that sails
   On the sea's brim
   Round the earth's rim
To the lilting of the gales;
   Of the sea horse
   That's a wee horse
And frolics in the sea
   'Neath the coral
   White and sorrel
That is the mermaids' tree;

And grazes on the seaweed
And the sea anemone;
But my ears cannot distinguish
The words it sings to me,
The sea shell,
The wee shell,
I hold so reverently,
And I only hear a whisper
Like the ghost voice of the sea.
—*Rowena Bastin Bennett*

THE OLD HORSE IN THE CITY

The moon's a peck of corn. It lies
Heaped up for me to eat.
I wish that I might climb the path
And taste that supper sweet.

Men feed me straw and scanty grain
And beat me till I'm sore.
Some day I'll break the halter-rope
And smash the stable-door,

Run down the street and mount the hill
Just as the corn appears.
I've seen it rise at certain times
For years and years and years.
—*Vachel Lindsay*

THE LIZARD

The Lizard is a funny thing.
   He has a snaky head,
A snaky tail beside,—and yet
   He is a quad-ru-ped.

He has a little lightning tongue
   With which he snaps the flies,
And yes,—there is a funny look
   About his fiery eyes!

I think he was a Dragon once,
   With great big pointed wings,
And wicked jaws and wicked claws,
   And teeth and scales and things.

I think a Hero sought him out,
   And fought an awful fight,
Then changed the Dragon by a spell
   Into this helpless mite.

I like to watch the Lizard bask.
   But oh! Suppose some day
The Dragon should change back again,—
   How fast I'd run away!
            —Abbie Farwell Brown

A MODERN DRAGON

A train is a dragon that roars through the dark.
He wriggles his tail as he sends up a spark.
He pierces the night with his one yellow eye,
And all the earth trembles when he rushes by.

—Rowena Bastin Bennett

ANIMAL FUN

Lumpskin, Ploshkin, Pelican jill!
We think so then, and we thought so still!

Edward Lear.

THE SHIP OF RIO

There was a ship of Rio
    Sailed out into the blue,
And nine and ninety monkeys
    Were all her jovial crew.
From bo'sun to the cabin boy,
    From quarter to caboose,
There weren't a stitch of calico
    To breech 'em—tight or loose;
From spar to deck, from deck to keel,
    From barnacle to shroud,
There weren't one pair of reach-me-downs
    To all that jabbering crowd.
But wasn't it a gladsome sight,
    When roared the deep-sea gales,
To see them reef her fore and aft,
    A-swinging by their tails!
Oh, wasn't it a gladsome sight,
    When glassy calm did come,
To see them squatting tailor-wise
    Around a keg of rum!
Oh, wasn't it a gladsome sight,
    When in she sailed to land,
To see them all a-scampering skip
    For nuts across the sand!
                    —Walter de la Mare

THE LION

The Lion, the Lion, he dwells in the waste,
He has a big head and a very small waist;
But his shoulders are stark, and his jaws they are grim,
And a good little child will not play with him.
                    —Hilaire Belloc

[149]

THE LION

The Lion is a kingly beast.
He likes a Hindu for a feast.
And if no Hindu he can get,
The lion-family is upset.

He cuffs his wife and bites her ears
Till she is nearly moved to tears.
Then some explorer finds the den
And all is family peace again.

—Vachel Lindsay

THE HIPPOPOTAMUS

I shoot the Hippopotamus with bullets made of platinum,
Because if I use leaden ones his hide is sure to flatten 'em.

—Hilaire Belloc

THE YAK

As a friend to the children commend me the Yak.
    You will find it exactly the thing:
It will carry and fetch, you can ride on its back,
    Or lead it about with a string.

The Tartar who dwells on the plains of Thibet
    (A desolate region of snow)
Has for centuries made it a nursery pet,
    And surely the Tartar should know!

Then tell your papa where the Yak can be got,
    And if he is awfully rich
He will buy you the creature—or else he will *not*.
    (I cannot be positive which.)

—Hilaire Belloc

TWO LITTLE KITTENS

Two little kittens, one stormy night,
  Began to quarrel and then to fight;
One had a mouse, and the other had none,
  And that's the way the quarrel begun.

"I'll have that mouse," said the bigger cat.
  "You'll have that mouse? We'll see about that!"
"I will have that mouse," said the eldest son.
  "You shan't have that mouse," said the little one.

I told you before, 'twas a stormy night,
  When these two little kittens began to fight;
The old woman seized her sweeping broom,
  And swept the two kittens right out of the room.

The ground was covered with frost and snow,
  And the two little kittens had nowhere to go;
So they laid themselves down on the mat by the door,
  While the old woman finished sweeping the floor.

Then they crept in, as quiet as mice,
  All wet with snow, and as cold as ice;
For they found it was better, that stormy night,
  To lie down and sleep, than to quarrel and fight.
                              —*Author Unknown*

KITTY CAUGHT A HORNET

  Kitty caught a hornet,
  Put it in a cage,
  Fed it burs and buttermilk,
  Got it in a rage;

[151]

Gave it lots of lettuce leaves,
Ice and smelling salts,
Whistled it a lively tune
And it began to waltz;
Gave it batting for a bed,
Snug and warm and deep,
Fanned it with a feather
And it went off to sleep.

—*Leroy F. Jackson*

THE THREE LITTLE KITTENS

Three little kittens lost their mittens;
And they began to cry,
"Oh, mother dear,
We very much fear
That we have lost our mittens."
"Lost your mittens!
You naughty kittens!
Then you shall have no pie!"
"Mee-ow, mee-ow, mee-ow."
"No, you shall have no pie."

The three little kittens found their mittens;
And they began to cry,
"Oh, mother dear,
See here, see here!
See, we have found our mittens!"
"Put on your mittens,
You silly kittens,

And you may have some pie."
　　"Purr-r, purr-r, purr-r,
Oh, let us have the pie!
　　Purr-r, purr-r, purr-r."

The three little kittens put on their mittens,
　　And soon ate up the pie;
　　　"Oh, mother dear,
　　　We greatly fear
That we have soiled our mittens!"
　　　"Soiled your mittens!
　　　You naughty kittens!"
Then they began to sigh,
　　　"Mee-ow, mee-ow, mee-ow."

The three little kittens washed their mittens,
　　And hung them out to dry;
　　　"Oh, mother dear,
　　　Do you not hear
That we have washed our mittens?"
　　　"Washed your mittens!
　　　Oh, you're good kittens!
But I smell a rat close by;
　　　Hush, hush! Mee-ow, mee-ow."
"We smell a rat close by,
　　　"Mee-ow, mee-ow, mee-ow."
　　　　　　　　—*Author Unknown*

THE LITTLE KITTENS

"Where are you going, my little kittens?"
"We are going to town to get us some mittens."
  "What! Mittens for kittens!
  Do kittens wear mittens?
Who ever saw little kittens with mittens?"

"Where are you going, my little cat?"
"I am going to town to get me a hat."
  "What! A hat for a cat!
  A cat get a hat!
Who ever saw a cat with a hat?"

"Where are you going, my little pig?"
"I am going to town to get me a wig."
  "What! A wig for a pig!
  A pig in a wig!
Who ever saw a pig in a wig?"
              —Eliza Lee Follen

VIEWPOINTS

Head-downward hung the bat;
  He looked on field and town.
"It's plain," he chittered, "that
  The world is upside-down!"

"How funny!" laughed the pup;
  "But then, it isn't true.
The world is rightside-up;
  What's upside-down, is *you!*
              —Arthur Guiterman

AN INCONVENIENCE

To his cousin the Bat
Squeaked the envious Rat,
"How fine to be able to fly!"
Tittered she, "Leather wings
Are convenient things;
But nothing *to sit on* have I."
                    —*John Banister Tabb*

AN INSECTARIAN

"I cannot wash my dog," she said,
    "Nor touch him with a comb,
For fear the fleas upon him bred
    May find no other home."
                    —*John Banister Tabb*

THE PUZZLED CENTIPEDE

A centipede was happy quite,
Until a frog in fun
Said, "Pray, which leg comes after which?"
This raised her mind to such a pitch,
She lay distracted in the ditch
Considering how to run.
                    —*Author Unknown*

FROGS AT SCHOOL

Twenty froggies went to school
Down beside a rushy pool;
Twenty little coats of green,
Twenty vests all white and clean.

"We must be in time," said they,
"First we study, then we play;
That is how we keep the rule,
When we froggies go to school."

Master Bullfrog, grave and stern,
Called the classes in their turn;
Taught them how to nobly strive,
Likewise how to leap and dive.

From his seat upon a log,
Showed them how to say, "Ker-chog!"
Also how to dodge a blow
From the sticks which bad boys throw.

Twenty froggies grew up fast;
Bullfrogs they became at last.
Not one dunce was in the lot,
Not one lesson they forgot.

Polished in a high degree,
As each froggy ought to be,
Now they sit on other logs,
Teaching other little frogs.

—*George Cooper*

HOW TO TELL THE WILD ANIMALS

If ever you should go by chance
   To jungles in the East;
And if there should to you advance
   A large and tawny beast,
If he roars at you as you're dyin'
You'll know it is the Asian Lion.

Or if sometime when roaming round,
   A noble wild beast greets you,
With black stripes on a yellow ground,
   Just notice if he eats you.
This simple rule may help you learn
The Bengal Tiger to discern.

If strolling forth, a beast you view,
   Whose hide with spots is peppered,
As soon as he has lept on you,
   You'll know it is the Leopard.
'Twill do no good to roar with pain,
He'll only lep and lep again.

If when you're walking round your yard,
   You meet a creature there,
Who hugs you very, very hard,
   Be sure it is the Bear.
If you have any doubt, I guess
He'll give you just one more caress.

Though to distinguish beasts of prey
   A novice might nonplus,
The Crocodiles you always may
   Tell from Hyenas thus:
Hyenas come with merry smiles;
But if they weep, they're Crocodiles.

The true Chameleon is small,
   A lizard sort of thing;
He hasn't any ears at all,
   And not a single wing.
If there is nothing on the tree,
'Tis the Chameleon you see.

              —*Carolyn Wells*

THE LOBSTER QUADRILLE

"Will you walk a little faster?" said a whiting to a snail,
"There's a porpoise close behind us, and he's treading on my
    tail.
See how eagerly the lobsters and the turtles all advance!
They are waiting on the shingle,—will you come and join
    the dance?
    Will you, won't you, will you, won't you, will you join
      the dance?
    Will you, won't you, will you, won't you, won't you join
      the dance?

"You can really have no notion how delightful it will be
When they take us up and throw us, with the lobsters, out
    to sea!"
But the snail replied, "Too far! Too far!" and gave a look
    askance,—
Said he thanked the whiting kindly, but he would not join
    the dance.
    Would not, could not, would not, could not, would not
      join the dance,
    Would not, could not, would not, could not, could not
      join the dance.

"What matters it how far we go?" his scaly friend replied,
"There is another shore, you know, upon the other side.
The further off from England the nearer is to France;
Then turn not pale, beloved snail, but come and join the
    dance.
    Will you, won't you, will you, won't you, will you join
      the dance?
    Will you, won't you, will you, won't you, won't you join
      the dance?"

—Lewis Carroll

THE OWL AND THE PUSSY-CAT

The Owl and the Pussy-Cat went to sea
  In a beautiful pea-green boat;
They took some honey, and plenty of money
  Wrapped up in a five-pound note.
The Owl looked up to the stars above,
  And sang to a small guitar,
"O, lovely Pussy! O, Pussy, my love,
  What a beautiful Pussy you are,
      You are,
      You are!
What a beautiful Pussy you are!"

Pussy said to the Owl, "You elegant fowl!
  How charmingly sweet you sing!
Oh! let us be married; too long we have tarried:
  But what shall we do for a ring?"
They sailed away, for a year and a day,
  To the land where the bong-tree grows;
And there in a wood a Piggy-wig stood
  With a ring at the end of his nose,
      His nose,
      His nose,
With a ring at the end of his nose.

"Dear Pig, are you willing to sell for one shilling
  Your ring?" Said the Piggy, "I will."
So they took it away, and were married next day
  By the Turkey who lives on the hill.

They dined on mince and slices of quince,
    Which they ate with a runcible spoon,
And hand in hand, on the edge of the sand,
    They danced by the light of the moon,
        The moon,
        The moon,
They danced by the light of the moon.

—*Edward Lear*

THE WONDERFUL MEADOW

Over in the meadow, in the sand, in the sun,
Lived an old Mother-Toad and her little toady one.
"Leap," said the mamma. "I'll leap," said the one,
And she leaped with her mamma in the sand, in the sun.

Over in the meadow, where the water runs blue,
Lived an old Mother-Fish and her little fishes two.
"Swim," said the mamma. "We'll swim," said the two,
And they swam and they danced in the water so blue.

Over in the meadow, in the old apple-tree,
Lived a Mother-Bluebird and her little birdies three.
"Sing," said the mamma. "We'll sing," said the three,
And they sang their sweet songs in the old apple-tree.

Over in the meadow, in the reeds on the shore,
Lived a Mother-Muskrat and her little ratties four.
"Dive," said the mamma. "We'll dive," said the four.
And they dove every day, 'mid the reeds on the shore.

Over in the meadow, in their snug little hive,
Lived a Mother-Honeybee, and the little bees were five.
"Buzz," said the mamma. "We'll buzz," said the five.
And they buzzed and made honey in their busy little hive.

Over in the meadow, in a nest built of sticks,
Lived a black Mother-Crow and her little blackies six.
"Caw," said the mamma. "We'll caw," said the six,
And they cawed and they cawed in their nest built of sticks.

Over in the meadow, in the calm summer even,
Lived a Mother-Firefly, and her little flies were seven.
"Shine," said the mamma. "We'll shine," said the seven,
And they shone like the stars, in the calm summer even.

Over in the meadow, on an old mossy gate,
Lived a Mother-Lizard, and her little lizards eight.
"Bask," said the mamma. "We'll bask," said the eight,
And they basked in the sun on the old mossy gate.

Over in the meadow, where the clear waters shine,
Lived a Mother-Bullfrog, and her little froggies nine.
"Croak," said the mamma. "We'll croak," said the nine,
And they croaked every night where the clear waters shine.

Over in the meadow, in her sly little den,
Lived a Mother-Spider, and her little spiders ten.
"Spin," said the mamma. "We'll spin," said the ten,
And they spun their lace webs in their little sly den.

Over in the meadow, where the grass is soft and even,
Lived a Mother-Cricket and her little ones eleven.
"Chirp," said the mamma. "We'll chirp," said the eleven,
And they chirped and they chirped where the grass is soft
    and even.

Over in the meadow, where the men dig and delve,
Lived an old Mother-Ant and her little anties twelve.
"Toil," said the mamma. "We'll toil," said the twelve,
And they toiled every day where the men dig and delve.

—*Olive A. Wadsworth*

THE MONKEYS AND THE CROCODILE

Five little monkeys
Swinging from a tree;
Teasing Uncle Crocodile,
Merry as can be.
Swinging high, swinging low,
Swinging left and right:
"Dear Uncle Crocodile,
Come and take a bite!"

Five little monkeys
Swinging in the air;
Heads up, tails up,
Little do they care.
Swinging up, swinging down,
Swinging far and near:
"Poor Uncle Crocodile,
Are n't you hungry, dear?"

Four little monkeys
Sitting in the tree;
Heads down, tails down,
Dreary as can be.
Weeping loud, weeping low,
Crying to each other:
"Wicked Uncle Crocodile,
To gobble up our brother!"
—*Laura E. Richards*

THE CROCODILE

Why does the crocodile weep, Mamma?
   Why does the crocodile weep?
He has a sorrow, dear my child;
It makes him sad, it makes him wild;
   He cannot be a sheep!

He cannot wag a woolly tail,
   He cannot say, "Ba! ba!"
He cannot jump, nor flimp nor flump,
   Nor gallop off afar.

Be sorry for the crocodile,
   But don't go very near;
Howe'er he bawl, whate'er befall,
   Don't try to dry his tear!
                —Laura E. Richards

THE DINKEY-BIRD

In an ocean, 'way out yonder
   (As all sapient people know),
Is the land of Wonder-Wander,
   Whither children love to go;
It's their playing, romping, swinging,
   That give great joy to me
While the Dinkey-Bird goes singing
   In the amfalula tree!

There the gum-drops grow like cherries,
   And taffy's thick as peas—
Caramels you pick like berries
   When, and where, and how you please;

Big red sugar-plums are clinging
   To the cliffs beside that sea
Where the Dinkey-Bird is singing
   In the amfalula tree.

So when children shout and scamper
   And make merry all the day,
When there's naught to put a damper
   To the ardor of their play;
When I hear their laughter ringing,
   Then I'm sure as sure can be
That the Dinkey-Bird is singing
   In the amfalula tree.

For the Dinkey-Bird's bravuras
   And staccatos are so sweet—
His roulades, appoggiaturas,
   And robustos so complete,
That the youth of every nation—
   Be they near or far away—
Have especial delectation
   In that gladsome roundelay.

Their eyes grow bright and brighter
   Their lungs begin to crow,
Their hearts get light and lighter,
   And their cheeks are all aglow;
For an echo cometh bringing
   The news to all and me,
That the Dinkey-Bird is singing
   In the amfalula tree.

I'm sure you like to go there
 To see your feathered friend—
And so many goodies grow there
 You would like to comprehend!
Speed, little dreams, your winging
 To that land across the sea
Where the Dinkey-Bird is singing
 In the amfalula tree!

      —Eugene Field

HURT NO LIVING THING

Hurt no living thing:
  Ladybird, nor butterfly,
Nor moth with dusty wing,
  Nor cricket chirping cheerily
Nor grasshopper so light of leap,
  Nor dancing gnat, nor beetle fat,
Nor harmless worms that creep.

Christina G. Rossetti.

A LINNET IN A GILDED CAGE

A linnet in a gilded cage,—
A linnet on a bough,—
In frosty winter one might doubt
Which bird is luckier now.

But let the trees burst out in leaf,
And nests be on the bough,—
Which linnet is the luckier bird,
Oh who could doubt it now?
—*Christina G. Rossetti*

TIT FOR TAT

Have you been catching of fish, Tom Noddy?
    Have you snared a weeping hare?
Have you whistled, "No Nunny," and gunned a poor bunny,
    Or a blinded bird of the air?

Have you trod like a murderer through the green woods,
    Through the dewy deep dingles and glooms,
While every small creature screamed shrill to Dame Nature,
    "He comes—and he comes!"?

Wonder I very much do, Tom Noddy,
    If ever, when you are a-roam,
An Ogre from space will stoop a lean face,
    And lug you home:

Lug you home over his fence, Tom Noddy,
    Of thorn-stocks nine yards high,
With your bent knees strung round his old iron gun
    And your head dan-dangling by:

And hang you up stiff on a hook, Tom Noddy,
  From a stone-cold pantry shelf,
Whence your eyes will glare in an empty stare,
  Till you are cooked yourself!
                  —Walter de la Mare

STUPIDITY STREET

I saw with open eyes
Singing birds sweet
Sold in the shops
For the people to eat,
Sold in the shops of
Stupidity Street.

I saw in vision
The worm in the wheat,
And in the shops nothing
For people to eat;
Nothing for sale in
Stupidity Street.
                  —Ralph Hodgson

THE BELLS OF HEAVEN

'Twould ring the bells of Heaven
The wildest peal for years,
If Parson lost his senses
And people came to theirs,
And he and they together
Knelt down with angry prayers
For tamed and shabby tigers
And dancing dogs and bears,
And wretched, blind pit ponies,
And little hunted hares.
                  —Ralph Hodgson

HOPPING FROG

Hopping frog, hop here and be seen,
  I'll not pelt you with stick or stone:
Your cap is laced and your coat is green;
  Good-bye, we'll let each other alone.

Plodding toad, plod here and be looked at,
You the finger of scorn is crooked at:
But though you're lumpish, you're harmless too;
You won't hurt me, and I won't hurt you.
                              —*Christina G. Rossetti*

LITTLE THINGS

  Little things, that run, and quail,
  And die, in silence and despair!

  Little things, that fight, and fail,
  And fall, on sea, and earth, and air!

  All trapped and frightened little things,
  The mouse, the coney, hear our prayer!

  As we forgive those done to us,
  —The lamb, the linnet, and the hare—

  Forgive us all our trespasses,
  Little creatures, everywhere!
                              —*James Stephens*

THE SNARE

I hear a sudden cry of pain!
There is a rabbit in a snare:
Now I hear the cry again,
But I cannot tell from where.

But I cannot tell from where
He is calling out for aid!
Crying on the frightened air,
Making everything afraid!

Making everything afraid!
Wrinkling up his little face!
As he cries again for aid;
—And I cannot find the place!

And I cannot find the place
Where his paw is in the snare!
Little One! Oh, Little One!
I am searching everywhere!

—*James Stephens*

THE BROWN THRUSH

There's a merry brown thrush sitting up in the tree.
  "He's singing to me! He's singing to me!"
And what does he say, little girl, little boy?
  "O, the world's running over with joy!
  Don't you hear? Don't you see?
    Hush! Look! In my tree
I'm as happy as happy can be!"

And the brown thrush keeps singing, "A nest do you see,
    And five eggs, hid by me in the juniper-tree?
Don't meddle! don't touch! little girl, little boy,
    Or the world will lose some of its joy!
        Now I'm glad! Now I'm free!
            And I always shall be,
If you never bring sorrow to me."

So the merry brown thrush sings away in the tree,
    To you and to me, to you and to me;
And he sings all the day, little girl, little boy,
    "O, the world's running over with joy!
        But long it won't be,
            Don't you know? don't you see?
Unless we are as good as can be?"

—Lucy Larcom

A ROBIN REDBREAST

A Robin Redbreast in a cage
Puts all Heaven in a rage. . . .

A Starling wounded in the wing,
A Cherubim does cease to sing. . . .

The wild Deer wandering here and there
Keeps the Human Soul from care. . . .

He who shall hurt the little Wren
Shall never be beloved by Men. . . .

The wanton Boy that kills the Fly
Shall feel the Spider's enmity. . . .

Kill not the Moth nor Butterfly,
For the Last Judgment draweth nigh;

The Beggar's Dog and Widow's Cat,
Feed them, and thou wilt grow fat. . . .

To see a World in a Grain of Sand,
And a Heaven in a Wild Flower,
Hold Infinity in the palm of your hand,
And Eternity in an hour.
                              —*William Blake*

COME
HOLIDAYS

H oliadys, vacation days and days to go to school,
Winter days and summer days and days of spring and fall,
To make the calendar, my dear, we have to take them all.

        Annette Wynne.

MEETING THE EASTER BUNNY

On Easter morn at early dawn
  before the cocks were crowing,
I met a bob-tail bunnykin
  and asked where he was going,
" 'Tis in the house and out the house
  a-tipsy, tipsy-toeing,
'Tis round the house and 'bout the house
  a-lightly I am going."
"But what is that of every hue
  you carry in your basket?"
" 'Tis eggs of gold and eggs of blue;
  I wonder that you ask it.
'Tis chocolate eggs and bonbon eggs
  and eggs of red and gray,
For every child in every house
  on bonny Easter Day."
He perked his ears and winked his eye
  and twitched his little nose;
He shook his tail—what tail he had—
  and stood up on his toes.
"I must be gone before the sun;
  the east is growing gray;
'Tis almost time for bells to chime."—
  So he hippety-hopped away.

—Rowena Bastin Bennett

A THANKSGIVING FABLE

It was a hungry pussy cat,
  Upon Thanksgiving morn,
And she watched a thankful little mouse
  That ate an ear of corn.

[177]

"If I ate that thankful little mouse,
  How thankful he should be,
When he has made a meal himself
  To make a meal for me!

"Then with his thanks for having fed,
  And his thanks for feeding me,
With all *his* thankfulness inside,
  How thankful I shall be!"

Thus "mewsed" the hungry pussy cat,
  Upon Thanksgiving Day;
But the little mouse had overheard
  And declined (with thanks) to stay.
                    —*Oliver Herford*

FOR CHRISTMAS

I want a Puppy Dog
Not made of wool.
I want a Kitty Cat
I don't have to wind.
I want a Nanny Goat
I don't have to pull;
And I want an Elephant
Can sit DOWN behind.
                    —*Dorothy Aldis*

SANTA CLAUS AND THE MOUSE

One Christmas eve, when Santa Claus
  Came to a certain house,
To fill the children's stockings there,
  He found a little mouse.

[178]

"A merry Christmas, little friend,"
  Said Santa, good and kind.
"The same to you, sir," said the mouse;
  "I thought you wouldn't mind

"If I should stay awake to-night
  And watch you for a while."
"You're very welcome, little mouse,"
  Said Santa, with a smile.

And then he filled the stockings up
  Before the mouse could wink—
From toe to top, from top to toe,
  There wasn't left a chink.

"Now, they won't hold another thing,"
  Said Santa Claus, with pride.
A twinkle came in mouse's eyes,
  But humbly he replied:

"It's not polite to contradict—
  Your pardon I implore—
But in the fullest stocking there
  I could put one thing more."

"Oh, ho!" laughed Santa, "silly mouse!
  Don't I know how to pack?
By filling stockings all these years,
  I should have learned the knack."

And then he took the stocking down
  From where it hung so high,
And said: "Now put in one thing more;
  I give you leave to try."

The mousie chuckled to himself,
  And then he softly stole
Right to the stocking's crowded toe
  And gnawed a little hole!

"Now, if you please, good Santa Claus,
  I've put in one thing more;
For you will own that little hole
  Was not in there before."

How Santa Claus did laugh and laugh!
  And then he gaily spoke:
"Well! you shall have a Christmas cheese
  For that nice little ioke."

If you don't think this story true,
  Why! I can show to you
The *very stocking* with the hole
  The little mouse gnawed through.
                    —*Emilie Poulsson*

A CHRISTMAS FOLK-SONG

The little Jesus came to town;
The wind blew up, the wind blew down;
Out in the street the wind was bold;
Now who would house Him from the cold?

Then opened wide a stable door,
Fair were the rushes on the floor;
The Ox put forth a hornèd head:
"Come, Little Lord, here make Thy bed."

Up rose the Sheep were folded near:
"Thou Lamb of God, come, enter here."
He entered there to rush and reed,
Who was the Lamb of God indeed.

The little Jesus came to town;
With ox and sheep He laid Him down;
Peace to the byre, peace to the fold,
For that they housed Him from the cold!
                    —*Lizette Woodworth Reese*

THE BARN

"I am tired of this barn," said the colt,
    "And every day it snows.
Outside, there's no grass any more
    And icicles grow on my nose.
I am tired of hearing the cows
    Breathing and talking together,
I'm sick of the clucking of hens,
    I hate stables and winter weather."

"Hush! little colt," said the mare,
    "And a story I will tell
Of a barn like this one of ours
    And the things that there befell.
It was weather much like this
    And the beasts stood as we stand now
In the warm, good dark of the barn—
    A horse and an ass and a cow."

"And sheep?" asked the colt. "Yes, sheep,
  And a pig and a goat and a hen.
All of the beasts of the barnyard,
  The usual servants of men.
And into their midst came a Lady,
  And she was as cold as death,
But the animals leaned above her
  And made her warm with their breath.

"There was her Baby born
  And laid to sleep in the hay,
While music flooded the rafters
  And the barn was as light as day,
And angels and kings and shepherds
  Came to worship the Babe from afar,
But we looked at Him first of all creatures
  By the bright, strange light of a star!"
                    —*Elizabeth Coatsworth*

SLEEPY SONGS

She sings me a queer little sleepy song,
Of sheep that go over a hill.
Josephine Daskam Bacon.

SLUMBER SONG

Drowsily come the sheep
From the place where the pastures be,
   By a dusty lane
   To the fold again,
First one, and then two, and three:
  First one, then two, by the paths of sleep
  Drowsily come the sheep.

Drowsily come the sheep,
And the shepherd is singing low:
   Up to eight and nine
   In an endless line,
They come, and then in they go.
  First eight, then nine, by the paths of sleep
  Drowsily come the sheep.

Drowsily come the sheep
And they pass through the sheepfold door;
   After one comes two,
   After one comes two,
Comes two, and then three and four.
  First one, then two, by the paths of sleep,
  Drowsily come the sheep.

—Louis V. Ledoux

THE SLEEPY SONG

As soon as the fire burns red and low,
And the house up-stairs is still,
She sings me a queer little sleepy song,
Of sheep that go over a hill.

The good little sheep run quick and soft,
Their colors are gray and white:
They follow their leader nose to tail,
For they must be home by night.

And one slips over and one comes next,
And one runs after behind,
The gray one's nose at the white one's tail,
The top of the hill they find.

And when they get to the top of the hill
They quietly slip away,
But one runs over and one comes next—
Their colors are white and gray.

And over they go, and over they go,
And over the top of the hill,
The good little sheep run quick and soft,
And the house up-stairs is still.

And one slips over and one comes next,
The good little, gray little sheep!
I watch how the fire burns red and low,
And she says that I fall asleep.

                              —*Josephine Daskam Bacon*

ACKNOWLEDGMENTS

For permission to reprint the poems included in *Under the Tent of the Sky* appreciation is expressed to the following publishers and authors:—

G. Bell & Sons, Ltd., London, for "A Friend in the Garden," from *Verses for Children* by Juliana Horatia Ewing.

Milton Bradley Company, Springfield, Massachusetts, for "Santa Claus and the Mouse," from *In the Child's World* by Emilie Poulsson.

Child Life Magazine; copyright Rand McNally and Company, and the authors for "Kitty Caught a Hornet," and "The Sea Gull," by Leroy F. Jackson; "My Airedale Dog," by W. L. Mason; "Our Circus," by Laura Lee Randall; and "Swimming," by Clinton Scollard.

Coward-McCann, Inc., New York, for "The Mouse," from *Compass Rose* by Elizabeth Coatsworth.

Dodd, Mead & Company, Inc., New York, for "How to Tell the Wild Animals," from *Baubles* by Carolyn Wells.

Doubleday, Doran & Company, Inc., New York, for "The Animal Store," from *Taxis and Toadstools* by Rachel Field (Copyright, 1926, by Doubleday, Doran & Company, Inc.); "The Cock," and "The Cuckoo," from *Fairies and Chimneys* by Rose Fyleman (Copyright, 1920, by Doubleday, Doran & Company, Inc.); "There Are No Wolves in England Now," and lines from "The Visit," from *The Fairy Green* by Rose Fyleman (Copyright, 1923, by Doubleday, Doran & Company, Inc.); "Bingo Has an Enemy," "If Only . . . ," "Shop Windows," "Temple Bar," and "Trafalgar Square," from *Gay Go Up* by Rose Fyleman (Copyright, 1929, 1930, by Doubleday, Doran & Company, Inc.); "The Canary," and "Timothy," from *The Fairy Flute* by Rose Fyleman (Copyright, 1923, by Doubleday, Doran & Company, Inc.); "Animal Crackers," and "The Moon-Sheep," from *Songs for a Little House* by Christopher Morley (Copyright, 1917, by Doubleday, Doran & Company, Inc.); and "The Blackbird," from *Kensington Gardens* by Humbert Wolfe (Reprinted by permission from Doubleday, Doran & Company, Inc.).

Gerald Duckworth & Company, Ltd., London, for "The Elephant," "The Hippopotamus," "The Lion," and "The Yak," from *The Bad Child's Book of Beasts* by Hilaire Belloc.

E. P. Dutton & Company, Inc., New York, for one line from "At the Zoo," from *When We Were Very Young* by A. A. Milne and for "Robin Redbreast," from *Poems and Prophesies* by William Blake, in Everyman's Library.

Follett Publishing Company, Chicago, for "Meeting the Easter Bunny," "A Modern Dragon," "The Rain," "Shell Castles," and "Under the Tent of the Sky," from *Around a Toadstool Table* by Rowena Bastin Bennett.

Harcourt, Brace and Company, Inc., New York, for "The Day of the Circus Horse," from *Selected Poems of T. A. Daly* (Copyright, 1936, by Harcourt, Brace and Company, Inc.); "Splinter," from *Good Morning, America* by Carl Sandburg (Copyright, 1928, by Carl Sandburg. By permission of Harcourt, Brace and Company, Inc.); "The Bear Hunt," and "The Looking-Glass Pussy," from *Little Girl and Boy Land* by Margaret Widdemer (Copyright, 1924, by Harcourt, Brace and Company, Inc.).

Harper & Brothers, New York, for "Viewpoints," from *The Light Guitar* and "The Boy and the Pup," from *The Laughing Muse* by Arthur Guiterman; "White Butterflies," by Charles Algernon Swinburne; "Familiar Friends," from *I Spend the Summer* by James S. Tippett; "Circus Parade," "Ducks at Dawn," "Spider Webs," and lines from "Let's Pretend," from *A World to Know* by James S. Tippett.

Henry Holt & Company, New York, for "Five Eyes," "Nicholas Nye," "Old Shellover," "The Ship of Rio," "Tit for Tat," and "Unstooping," from *Collected Poems 1901–1918* by Walter de la Mare; "The Pasture," and "Stopping by Woods on a Snowy Evening," from *Collected Poems of Robert Frost*.

Houghton Mifflin Company, Boston, for "The Brown Bear," from *The Children Sing in the Far West* by Mary Austin; "The Lizard," from *Songs of Sixpence* by Abbie Farwell Brown; "The Plaint of the Camel," from *Davy and the Goblin* by Charles Edward Carryl; "Fable," from *The Poetical Works of Ralph Waldo Emerson*; "The Brown Thrush," and "Red Top and Timothy," from *The Poetical Works of Lucy Larcom*; "Jester Bee," and "The Snow-Bird," from *Little-Folk Lyrics* by Frank Dempster Sherman; and "The Sandpiper," and "Wild Geese," from *Stories and Poems for Children* by Celia Thaxter. Each of these selections is used by permission of, and by arrangement with, Houghton Mifflin Company.

Alfred A. Knopf, Inc., New York, for "The Snail," from *Flying Fish* by Grace Hazard Conkling.

J. B. Lippincott Company, Philadelphia, for "Saturday Towels," from *Poems for Peter* by Lysbeth Boyd Borie.

Little, Brown & Company, Boston, for "The Worm," from *Jane, Joseph, and John* by Ralph Bergengren, an Atlantic Monthly Press publication; "A Bird Came Down the Walk," from *The Poems of Emily Dickinson*, Centenary Edition, edited by Martha Dickinson Bianchi and Alfred

[188]

Leete Hampson; "The Crocodile," and "The Monkeys and the Crocodile," from *Tirra Lirra: Rhymes Old and New* by Laura E. Richards.

Lothrop, Lee & Shepard Company, Boston, for "Wild Beasts," from
Child Songs of Cheer by Evaleen Stein, and "The Little Kittens," from
Little Songs by Eliza Lee Follen.

Robert M. McBride & Company, New York, for "Moth Miller," and
"The Race," from *The Coffee-Pot Face* by Aileen Fisher.

The Macmillan Company, New York, for "Robin Redbreast," from
Robin Redbreast and Other Poems by William Allingham; "The Ele-
phant," and "The Hairy Dog," from *Pillicock Hill* by Herbert Asquith;
"My Dog," from *Foothills of Parnassus* by John Kendrick Bangs; "A Cir-
cus Garland," from *Branches Green* and "Merry-Go-Round," from *The
Pointed People* by Rachel Field; "A Chinese Nursery Rhyme," from
Home Life in China by Isaac Headland; "The Bells of Heaven," and
"Stupidity Street," from *Poems* by Ralph Hodgson; "A Dirge for a
Righteous Kitten," "An Explanation of the Grasshopper," "The Lion,"
"The Little Turtle," "The Mysterious Cat," "The Old Horse in the
City," "The Humble Bumble Bee," and "What Grandpa Mouse Said,"
from *Collected Poems* by Vachel Lindsay; "Camel," "Cat," and "Lion,"
from *Menagerie* by Mary Britton Miller; "Brown and Furry," "The City
Mouse and the Garden Mouse," "Hopping Frog," "Horses of the Sea,"
"Hurt No Living Thing," "A Linnet in a Gilded Cage," "On the Grassy
Banks," and "When the Cows Come Home," from *Sing-Song* by Christina
G. Rossetti; "Little Things," "The Rivals," and "The Snare," from *Col-
lected Poems* by James Stephens; "Green Moth," from *Skipping Along
Alone* by Winifred Welles.

Macrae Smith Company, Philadelphia, for "The Teapot Dragon," from
All Round Our House by Rupert Sargent Holland.

Minton, Balch and Company, New York, for "Flies," and "Radiator
Lions," from *Everything and Anything*; "For Christmas," and "The
Grasshoppers," from *Here, There and Everywhere*; and "At The Circus,"
and "In the Barnyard," from *Hop, Skip and Jump* by Dorothy Aldis.

Thomas Bird Mosher, Portland, Maine, for "A Christmas Folk-Song,"
from *A Wayside Lute* by Lizette Woodworth Reese.

The *New York Times*, New York, for "Why Read a Book?" by
Colette M. Burns.

Oxford University Press, London, for "White Horses," from *Out of
the Everywhere* by Winifred Howard.

St. Nicholas Magazine, New York, for "Holding Hands," by Lenore
M. Link; and "The Monkeys," by Edith Osborn Thompson.

Scholastic Corporation, New York, for "Wind-Wolves," by William D.
Sargent from *Saplings*, 1926 series.

Charles Scribner's Sons, New York, for "The Sleepy Song," from

Poems by Josephine Daskam Bacon; "The Dinkey Bird," and "The Duel," from *The Poems of Eugene Field;* "Ducks' Ditty," from *The Wind in the Willows* by Kenneth Grahame; "The Elf and the Dormouse," from *Artful Antics;* "The Milk Jug," from *The Kitten's Garden of Verses,* "The Snail's Dream," from *The Bashful Earthquake,* and "A Thanksgiving Fable," by Oliver Herford; "The Cow," and "Time to Rise," from *A Child's Garden of Verses* by Robert Louis Stevenson.

Frederick A. Stokes Company, New York, for "Little Snail," from *Poems by a Little Girl* by Hilda Conkling (Copyright, 1920, by Frederick A. Stokes Company); "About Animals," from *Shoes of the Wind* by Hilda Conkling (Copyright, 1922, by Frederick A. Stokes Company); "Circus," from *Joan's Door* by Eleanor Farjeon (Copyright, 1926, by Frederick A. Stokes Company); "The Milk-cart Pony," and "Mrs. Peck-Pigeon," from *Over the Garden Wall* by Eleanor Farjeon (Copyright, 1933, by Eleanor Farjeon); "Excuse Us, Animals in the Zoo," from *All through the Year* by Annette Wynne (Copyright, 1932, by Annette Wynne); "I Wonder If the Lion Knows," "Lions Running over the Green," "Little Folks in the Grass," "People Buy a Lot of Things," from *For Days and Days: A Year-round Treasury of Verse for Children* by Annette Wynne (Copyright, 1919, by Frederick A. Stokes Company), "Little Charlie Chipmunk" from *Animal Etiquette Book* by Helen Cowles Le Cross (Copyright, 1926, by Frederick A. Stokes Company), and for "The Cow," and "The Sheep," from *The "Original Poems" and Others* by Ann Taylor.

The Viking Press, Inc., New York, for "Lone Dog," from *Songs to Save a Soul,* by Irene Rutherford McLeod (Copyright, 1919, by B. W. Heubsch, Inc.); "The Circus," "Firefly," "The Hens," "Horse," "Milking Time," "The Rabbit," "The Wolves," "The Woodpecker," and "The Worm," from *Under the Tree* by Elizabeth Madox Roberts (Copyright, 1922 and 1930).

Frederick Warne & Co., Inc., New York, for "The Owl and the Pussy Cat" by Edward Lear.

The Yale Review, New Haven, Connecticut, for lines from "Go to the Barn with a Lantern," by Robert P. Tristram Coffin.

Yale University Press, New Haven, Connecticut, for "Chanticleer," and "Serious Omission," from *Songs for Parents* by John Farrar.

Elizabeth Coatsworth and the *New York Herald Tribune* for "The Barn."

Elizabeth Coatsworth and *Story Parade* for "Sitting Here."

Georgia Roberts Durston for "The Hippopotamus," and "The Wolf."

Ethel Romig Fuller and Willett, Clark & Company, Chicago, for "Wind Is a Cat," from *White Peaks and Green.*

Louis V. Ledoux for "Slumber Song."

Dr. Francis A. Litz for "The Bluebeard," "Butterfly," "The Firefly," "An Inconvenience," "An Insectarian," "The Pleiads," "The Tax-Gatherer," and "The Woodpecker," from *The Poetry of Father Tabb*.

Irene M. Mason and *Child Life Magazine* for "My Airedale Dog," by W. L. Mason, reprinted from *Child Life Magazine*; copyright Rand McNally and Company.

Katharine D. Morse for "A Bee Sets Sail," and "The Fairy Frock," from *A Gate of Cedar*.

Anne Blackwell Payne for "Fairy Aeroplanes," and "Silver Sheep"; and the author and the *New York Sun* for "At Night," by Anne Blackwell Payne.

Virginia Rice for "Cat," and "Rabbits," from *I Like Animals* by Dorothy Baruch, published by Harper & Brothers, New York.

INDEX OF AUTHORS

[194]

[195]

INDEX OF TITLES

INDEX OF FIRST LINES

[203]